JAMES ARTHUR FOUNDATION

NEW YORK UNIVERSITY

*

TIME AND ITS MYSTERIES

TIME

and Its Mysteries

SERIES I

Four Lectures

given on the JAMES ARTHUR FOUNDATION

New York University

BY

ROBERT A. MILLIKAN

JOHN C. MERRIAM

HARLOW SHAPLEY

JAMES H. BREASTED

New York University Press

Washington Square, New York

London: Humphrey Milford • Oxford University Press

1936

Printed in the United States of America

NEW YORK UNIVERSITY
JAMES ARTHUR FOUNDATION

*

CONTENTS

LIST OF ILLUSTRATIONS

FOREWORD

IN PRESENTING the first four in what we believe will be a
notable series of lectures on the James Arthur Foundation
at New York University, a brief word of introduction is in
order. When, by his will, Mr. James Arthur created this
lectureship, he provided for the continuing study of a subject which had long fascinated him and to which he had
made notable contributions. "Time and Its Measurement,"
as the founder suggests in his own volume under that title,
is an elusive entity, as yet undefined. That men should study
the subject in the light of its historic significance and its
philosophic implications seemed to him both desirable and
feasible. He had already donated his unique collection of
timepieces to the University, giving to this institution not
only one of the most valuable of such collections in existence, but one in which the skill of the collector had assem-
bled representative pieces of the various stages in the evolution of time-measurement from its beginning. To these he
had added many notable examples of his own mechanical
and inventive genius. Through the generous endowment for
this collection, provided by Mr. Arthur, its upkeep and
enlargement are perpetuated; but much of the value of such
a veritable museum of timekeeping is immeasurably increased by the establishment of the lectureship, of which
this volume is the first fruit.

The possibilities in such a foundation are amply exempli-
fied by the four lectures presented herewith. Dr. Robert A.

Millikan, Dr. John C. Merriam, Dr. Harlow Shapley, and Dr. James H. Breasted[1] have set a very high standard, which gives this series a most auspicious beginning. The University is grateful to these distinguished scientists who have so graciously coöperated with its committee, both in the delivery and in the publication of these lectures.

IRVING H. BERG

Chairman, the Council's Committee on
the James Arthur Foundation

---

[1]While this volume was being prepared, the scientific world sustained a great loss in the death of Dr. James H. Breasted, who had submitted his manuscript for this publication but died before proofs could be sent to him.

TIME

TIME

Robert A. Millikan

To THE ordinary modern man nothing is simpler than the idea of time. He had a Waterbury watch for a Christmas present by the time he was six. He timed horse races or hundred-yard dashes or bicycle speeds to a fifth of a second with a stop watch before he was twelve. Through all his life he has gone to classes, eaten his meals, caught his trains—or missed them—by the clock. To him, therefore, time is a perfectly simple, completely understood, common-sense concept which has always been with the race and always will be.

But is this complacent, common-sense view of the ordinary hard-headed citizen sound or unsound? Or was, perhaps, the Mad Hatter in *Alice in Wonderland* nearer right when he said:

"If you knew Time as well as I do, you wouldn't talk about wasting *it*. It's *him*."

"I don't know what you mean," said Alice.

"Of course you don't!" the Hatter said, tossing his head contemptuously. "I dare say you never even spoke to Time!"

"Perhaps not," Alice cautiously replied; "but I know I have to beat time when I learn music."

"Ah! That accounts for it," said the Hatter. "He won't

stand beating, Now, if you only kept on good terms with him, he'd do almost anything you liked with the clock. For instance, suppose it were nine o'clock in the morning, just time to begin lessons: you'd only have to whisper a hint to Time, and round goes the clock in a twinkling! Half-past one, time for dinner!"

("I only wish it was," the March Hare said to itself in a whisper.)

"That would be grand, certainly," said Alice thoughtfully; "but then—I shouldn't be hungry for it, you know."

"Not at first, perhaps," said the Hatter; "but you could keep it to half-past one as long as you liked."

Now the question I am raising tonight is, How mad was the Hatter anyway when he gave the sort of changeable, un-dependable capricious qualities to Time which we assign to personality, and, playing deliciously upon our current phrases "beating time" and "murdering time," insisted on addressing Time as Him? Who is the nearer right, the Mad Hatter or the common-sense citizen?

Well, at any rate, this common-sense citizen has not always been right. Let me illustrate first how penetrating a judgment he has sometimes had by quoting from Robert Recorde's "Master and Scholar" dialogues published in the year 1556, thirteen years after the first publication of the Copernican thesis, which was: "That the earth not only moveth circularlye about his own centre, but also may be, yea and is continually out of the precise centre 38 hundredth thousand miles." This thesis is met with the typical reaction by the scholar, who says, "Nay syr in good faith, I desire not

Time

to heare such vaine phantasies, so farre against common reason, and repugnante to the consente of all the learned multitude of Wryters, and therefore let it passe for ever, and a daye longer."

Nor, indeed, were such common-sense judgments confined to the practical English, for some French verses translated in 1591, forty-eight years after Copernicus's publication, similarly assert satirically,

> Those clerks that think—think how absurd a jest!
> That neither heavens nor stars do turn at all,
> Nor dance around this great round earthly ball,
> But the earth itself, this massy globe of our's,
> Turn's round about once every twice twelve hours!
> And we resemble land-bred navvies
> New brought aboard to venture on the seas;
> Who at first launching from the shore suppose
> The ship stands still and that the firm earth goes.

What are the historic facts, then, about this idea of time? Here are some of them.

Like much else in this changing world, time, as you and I understand and use it, is a relatively new idea, just beginning to come into use in the fifteenth and sixteenth centuries, A.D. But in order not to be misunderstood, I must explain just what I mean by the phrase "time as you and I understand and use it."

For certain limited types of purposes, time began to be not only used but accurately measured at the very dawn of history. Indeed the first reliable date in history, according to Breasted, is 4241 B.C., or 6,173 years ago, and it is fixed by observations made in Egypt upon the star Sirius. Civilization presumably arose in Egypt, but eons before its rise, indeed from the very first appearance of life on the earth, the day was clearly marked by nature herself as the most fundamental and the most simple measure of time; for physiological processes of all sorts in plant, insect, fish, bird, beast, and human reveal a period determined by the rising of the sun. But from that point of view that other unit, the year, has almost equal claim, for ever since "the sap began to stir in April" the return of spring has been marked as a natural measure of time.

Now the beginnings of science are nearly always found in the first steps taken toward refining and making more precise natural but inaccurately defined concepts like those of the day and the year, and it was in this case the year rather than the day that first received in Egypt an exact quantitative definition. For the annual inundations of the Nile happened to coincide very nearly with the heliacal rising of Sirius, *i.e.*, the rising just before the dawn, so that his first appearance on the horizon in advance of the sun was taken to announce the new year, and this appearance (which otherwise stated marks quite accurately the annual return of the sun to a fixed point in the heavens) enabled those early Egyptians in the very dawn of history to measure the duration of the year as 365 days. In the matter of the length of the year, then, there is nothing new about time at all.

Also with the foregoing start, the Egyptians oriented their temples and pyramids so that some of them at least became time-measuring instruments. For example, the Great Pyramid was so carefully placed as to serve as an instrument for the determination of the time of the equinoxes, for on these

From Borchardt *Altägyptische Zeitmessung,* by courtesy of the Metropolitan Museum of Art

Figure 1. Egyptian sundial probably of the period of
Merneptah (13th century B.C.)

days its east and west faces were just grazed by the rays of the rising or setting sun. More than this, the Egyptians definitely had sundials or sun clocks, one form of which, quite like the conventional sundial, is shown in Figure 1 (facing page 6), while another form is seen in Figure 2 (facing page 8).

It will be correctly inferred from these illustrations that the modern division of the day into twelve hours and of the hour into sixty minutes and the minute into sixty seconds comes down to us from the earliest Egyptian times. Indeed, the antiquity of the origins both of our present time-measurement system and of our angle-measurement system is attested by the fact that these are the only surviving relics of the old sexagesimal notation which prevailed generally before the decimal system was finally adopted.

But at night what did the Egyptians do about time measurement? They had two solutions. The priests had rather elaborate categories of stars the positions of which told the time at a given season. This system, however, must have been so awkward because of the rapidly changing relations of solar and sidereal time that it is likely that it was used only by the experts.

The second method involved the use of the Egyptian water clock illustrated in Figure 3. The water was drained out through a small pipe, and the form of the vessel was so chosen as to give an equal fall of water per hour. These Egyptian water clocks had enough volume to enable the water to flow all night. The Greek and Roman variants of this device called clepsydra were actually used chiefly to set a limit to the speeches in the courts of justice, hence the terms *aquam dare*, to give speaking time, or *aquam perdere*, to waste time.

But in spite of the profound knowledge of stellar movement and its time-measuring capabilities herewith revealed, and in spite of the ingenuity shown by the expert in the development and perfection of water clocks, I repeat that in ancient times neither the expert nor the man on the streets had ever been introduced to time as we moderns know it. No Roman or Greek doctor ever counted his patient's pulse or took his temperature to find how sick he was.[1] Both watches and thermometers came with the ushering in some three or four hundred years ago of a new era. In the Roman Empire the ordinary man measured time at night by the first or the second crowing of the cock.

The Olympic victor led the field but nobody knew whether he won the hundred-yard dash in nine, ten, eleven, or forty seconds. Nowhere in the ancient world could a common citizen be late to breakfast on a cloudy morning, since without the sun there could be no definite breakfast hour. If the family planned a picnic no barometer foretold the lifting of the clouds or warned that rain was imminent. If one of the children was anemic no blood count could indicate that fact for the ancient world had no microscopes, nor telescopes either. Those were indeed simple days, for all

[1] This is strictly true with reference to the temperature, but needs this qualification with respect to the pulse beat. There is evidence that the clepsydra was sometimes used by Greek doctors for pulse counting, awkward and inexact though it was for such a purpose in comparison with our watches.

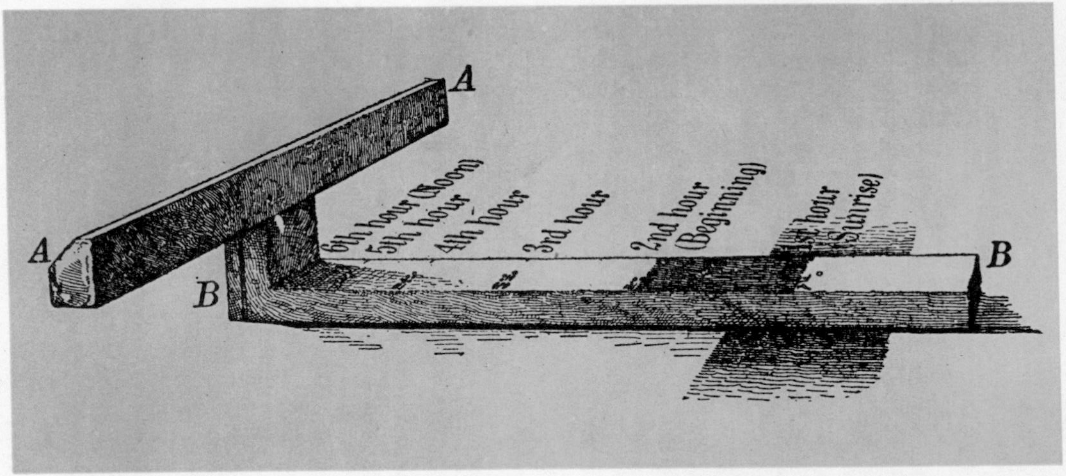
A
A
B
B
6th hour (Noon)
5th hour
4th hour
3rd hour
2nd hour
(Beginning)
1st hour
(Sunrise)

By courtesy of the Oriental Institute, The University of Chicago

Figure 2. Ancient Egyptian sun clock

The shadow of the crosspiece (*AA*), turned toward the East in the morning and toward the West after noon, indicated the hour on the arm (*BB*)

Time

our most important and most familiar measuring instruments, such as the clock, the barometer, the thermometer, the telescope, the microscope, first came into use in the sixteenth and seventeenth centuries A.D. Why?

I think the answer to the question is found in the fact that a new conception of the significance of time began then for the first time to arise in human thought—a conception that made practically every physical constant dependent upon a time-measurement with a clock or a watch or its equivalent. Galileo, sitting there in front of his inclined plane and his marbles, and first feeling the necessity of measuring the time-rate-of-change in their positions and in their velocities as they rolled down the plane—this typifies the whole new idea, for here was laid the basis of mechanics. To lay the first stone in the foundations of that mechanics it was necessary to have a timepiece, and Galileo himself is recognized as the inventor of the pendulum clock although he only used it practically, so we are told, for counting the pulse of his patients—the same patients whose temperatures he measured through his invention of the thermometer. The pulse itself, however, under normal conditions can serve and I believe actually did serve him as a short-interval timepiece.

However, the generally accepted history of the introduction of mechanical clocks is as follows: They seem to have begun to come into use in the thirteenth century. If invented earlier they were merely curiosities and they remained practically this until about 1600. A clock was actually put up in a former clock tower at Westminster with some great bells in 1288. These bells were sold or rather gambled away, it is said, by Henry VIII. Also a clock very much like the later pendulum clocks except that it was driven by a vibrating balance instead of a pendulum was made for the French King Charles V in 1379. About 1600 Galileo discovered the isochronism of the pendulum and although he made no practical use of it except in inventing the above mentioned instrument for measuring pulse beats, actually pendulum clocks came rapidly into general use immediately thereafter.

But in any event the need of measuring accurately through short intervals the time-rate-of-change of position, which is velocity, and again time-rate-of-change of velocity, which in its turn is acceleration and which was found by direct experiment to be an accurate measure of force, was the need that Galileo was the first to feel and to set carefully at work to try to satisfy; and out of it all came a whole new world concept, or better two new world concepts; namely, first, the concept of the uniformity of nature or the concept of natural law, and, second, the concept of the continuity of nature or more specifically the concept of the necessary continuity of motion and of change of motion.

Let me try to appraise the significance for human life of the introduction of these two ideas. The first, namely, the idea of the uniformity of nature, is what primarily distinguishes the modern world from the ancient. It grew out of accurate measurements on time-rates-of-change with clocks or their equivalent—measurements the like of which were never made in the ancient world. These measurements first

Time

established certain mechanical laws which, if true, rendered the accurate prediction of some astronomical events, like eclipses, and some terrestrial phenomena, like the paths of projectiles, the stability of structures, the speeds of railway trains or airplanes, etc., a possibility. The agreement between such calculations and direct experiment is what in time has convinced the world of the essential correctness of the Galilean and Newtonian postulates at least so far as macroscopic or large-scale events are concerned. It transformed this world from one that is at bottom capricious and animistic, as was in fact both the ancient world and the medieval one, to a world that is dependable and in part, at least, knowable and controllable by man—a stupendous change in outlook and significant evidence of the enormous influence of outlook on human life and conduct.

You will then agree with me that these ancient and medieval worlds had never, in the language of the Mad Hatter, been introduced to Time. The vague general common-sense notion of time that prevailed up to 1600 A.D. needed to be refined, sharpened, and rendered precise through the invention of precision time-measuring instruments applicable to short time-intervals before it acquired the power to change man's thought and life and to create a modern as distinct from an ancient or a medieval world.

The second element in the change in the time-concept that came in about 1600 A.D. I called above the concept of the continuity of nature. The Galilean and Newtonian world saw a constant force like gravitation producing a constant and continuous rate of change in velocity. To handle the problems of that world Newton and Leibnitz invented the calculus which Newton christened fluxions, *i.e.*, flowings or continuous changes. In a word the Galilean and Newtonian world is described by differential equations, its four independent variables being x, y, z, and t, t being completely independent of anything that happens to the observer so far as x, y, and z are concerned, and up to about the beginning of the twentieth century this concept of time as something quite independent of space coördinates had had an enormous number of successes and no failures. Our whole mechanical world governed by mechanical laws grew out of it. To the man on the streets and to the man in the laboratory, too, it was a simple, common-sense idea that a Seth Thomas clock which had been so beautifully adjusted as to come around repeatedly to 12 midnight when on successive nights a given star crosses the meridian should tick off absolute seconds. What more could the Mad Hatter want us to know about time than that? That was the time of the nineteenth century which made all measurements depend in the last analysis upon three absolute independent quantities — length, mass, and time.

Then came in 1887 the famous Michelson-Morley experiment which by 1905, as soon as its experimental correctness had become recognized, spoiled all this sense of completeness and infallibility in our fundamental thinking about the absoluteness of time. What is this Michelson-Morley experiment and why has it started such a ferment in physical thinking, a ferment which seeps down to the masses and causes even the yellow journal to attempt to follow the mod-

Figure 3. Egyptian water clock of the period of Amenhotep III
(about B.C. 1400)

The water was drained out through a small pipe and the twelve hours of the night
were indicated by its level on scales inscribed on the inner face

ern developments in relativity? Let me explain it by citing
a bit of history.

Throughout the whole of the nineteenth century we had
been building up, on the basis, too, of the Galilean-New-
tonian postulate of the continuousness of natural processes,
correctly describable by an expression $\frac{dx}{dt}$ even when the dx
and dt were taken infinitely small, a wonderfully consistent
"natural philosophy" as to the nature of radiant energy—a
beautiful wave-theory of light—a theory, too, that had predicted with extraordinary success even phenomena of such
analytical intricacy as conical refraction, for example. Any
one brought up as I was upon Michelson interferometers
and all the manifold variety of the facts of interference in
the fields of light, heat, and wireless waves, all beautifully
predicted by the ether-wave equations and now familiar to
every fifteen-year-old wireless enthusiast, had no shadow of
doubt as to the fundamental correctness of that wave theory.
This theory required that it be possible, by noting the time
required for a beam of light to get back to the observer
when, on the one hand, it was sent forth in the direction of
the earth's motion and back by reflection from a mirror to
the observer and when, on the other hand, it was sent a like
distance forth and back at right angles to the earth's motion,
to find the speed with which the earth is moving through
space. The reasoning is altogether simple and direct as the
corresponding imaginary experiments with sound waves will
show. Suppose a man facing east has a cliff a mile east of
him and another cliff a mile south of him. If he emits a note
and, while doing so, runs east to meet the echo from the

east cliff he will obviously hear it a little before he receives the echo from the south cliff the distance of which from him has remained constant. This experiment so described works just as it should whether tried with sound or with light. It is essentially the way we actually do, now, measure the relative speed of approach of the earth and a star, though in this case the light is emitted by the star instead of being reflected from it; but this is not an essential difference as is shown by measurements on planets which shine only by reflected light. We actually measure quite accurately the rotation period of Saturn by the difference in the relative times of arrival or differences in wave lengths of light waves coming from the limb that is moving toward us and the limb moving away from us.

But now suppose the observer and the two cliffs were on a huge moving platform traveling toward the east through still air. Then the echo from the east cliff would in this case clearly get back *after*, not before, the echo from the south cliff as can easily be seen by imagining the platform to be moving with the speed with which sound travels, for then the sound wave obviously could not reach the east cliff at all so that the echo from it would be infinitely delayed. Now in the Michelson experiment the moving platform was in fact the earth and he expected the light echo from the east cliff to get back after the echo from the south cliff. But in fact the expected time difference did not appear. The two echoes got back at exactly the same time. For twenty years we tried vainly to "understand" this result but we failed completely to get a reasonable explanation of it along

Time

classical lines. There was and there is now no understanding of it except through giving up the idea of absolute time and of absolute length and making the two interdependent concepts. But this overthrows the rigidity and the theoretical perfectness of the whole of mechanics. This is why relativity interests every one. Specifically, the length of the measuring rod when it was measuring the distance to the east cliff, *i.e.*, in the direction of motion through space, was assumed by Lorentz and Fitzgerald to be shorter than when the same rod was measuring the distance to the south cliff. In other words its length l depended upon the speed of its motion through space, but since speed $= \frac{dl}{dt}$ this meant that l and t, length and time, were not independent quantities. They might be considered as independent for bodies at rest or for bodies in relative motion with speeds small compared with the speed of light but not for bodies whose relative speeds were comparable with the speed of light.

It is indeed now no longer customary to talk about "the Lorentz-Fitzgerald shortening" of the measuring rod in the direction of motion as I have done above, though this is by far the simplest way of seeing the actual requirements of the Michelson-Morley experiment with respect to the space and time concepts. The reason for dropping this mode of approach is merely that Einstein in 1905 incorporated the results of the Michelson-Morley experiment into the first postulate of the special theory of relativity; that is, he generalized our experimental inability to find a speed of the earth with respect to the ether—or with respect to space if one prefers that expression—into the postulate that no abso-

Time and Its Mysteries

lute frame of reference for motion can be found, the *relative* motion of two bodies alone being measurable, the speed of a light signal always coming out a constant independent of the state of rest or motion of the body on which it is being measured. This postulate, precisely like that of the Lorentz-Fitzgerald shortening, denies the possibility of realizing absolute time or absolute speed and links time and space together into a composite space-time concept. So as to leave no experimental stone unturned in this most fundamental field, Drs. Roy S. Kennedy and Edward L. Thorndyke have, during the past four years, carried out and recently concluded at the Norman Bridge Laboratory at Pasadena a most accurate modification of the Michelson-Morley experiment in which the length of the two light paths and hence the two times of travel of the two light beams are entirely different, instead of being essentially the same as they have been in all preceding repetitions of this experiment. They have thus brought forward a new and more direct and very exact experimental proof of the relativity of *time* as well as of space.

Three hundred years, then, after the first establishment of the mechanical laws upon which the modern world is built, laws which take time and space as independent variables and which assign continuity to nature by describing her in terms of differential equations assumed to be valid no matter how small the time and space intervals are taken, these new nineteenth-century discoveries and viewpoints begin to raise seriously the question as to whether the Mad Hatter was not right when he attributed at bottom variable, even whimsical, qualities to time.

Time

But it is not the development of relativity so much as the development of the facts and the theory of quanta that has given Time the worst beating. The experimental discoveries of this century in the fields of photoelectric effects, Compton effects, X-ray and cosmic-ray effects, and spectroscopic effects have practically forced us to describe the physical world in terms of particles—particles or units of electrical charge which we call positive and negative electrons, particles or units of mass which we call protons and electrons, particles or units of radiant energy which we call photons, and particles or units of action (or momentum) which we call Planck's h units. Such a description of the physical world cannot be made in terms of differential equations. Macroscopic phenomena, in which large numbers of these units are involved, can of course still be described in terms of such differential equations just as may the outflow of sand from a truckload of it, for here the units—the sand grains— are so small that they do not appear as such to the rough measuring instruments that we use. It is only in the field of macroscopic phenomena that the Galilean and Newtonian mechanical laws have had such amazing successes during the past centuries. But in this twentieth century we have been studying for the first time microscopic phenomena in which only one or two or at any rate a relatively small number of these units have been involved and in all such cases we have found the mechanical laws breaking down, thus showing the extreme danger of extending generalizations outside the range in which observational checks have been or can be obtained.

Time and Its Mysteries

The final result to date of all these studies of microscopic phenomena is summed up in the so-called Heisenberg principle of uncertainty which says in essence that it is impossible to increase the accuracy of measurement of the *velocity* of a particle without by this very observational act introducing an uncertainty into the determination of the *position* of the particle, the law governing this uncertainty being that the product of the uncertainty in the measurement of the velocity (more accurately the momentum) by the uncertainty in the measurement of the position is always equal to Planck's constant h. Another way of stating the same thing is that the product of the uncertainty in the measurement of the *energy* of a particle by the uncertainty in the measurement of the *time* at which it had that energy is again equal to Planck's h.

From two quite different points of view, then, *i.e.*, from the observed facts of relativity and from the observed facts of quanta, the first obtained from studying bodies moving with extraordinarily high speeds, speeds comparable with the speed of light, the second obtained from studying microscopic phenomena or unitary elementary processes, physics has come to the conclusion that velocity and position, or energy and time, or more simply, length and time, are not at bottom independent of each other; in other words that there is no such thing as absolute time nor indeed as absolute length, and therefore that in the world of *elementary* processes there is no possibility of predicting, to use now old-time terminology, what is going to happen to a particular electron, or atom, or light-quant at a particular

Time

future instant of time from any observations of what has happened to this electron, atom, or light-quant at any preceding instant.

This means that philosophic determinism which has always been a presumptuous and a scientifically unwarranted generalization is now shown by experimental physics itself to be a false generalization. How Laplace would turn in his grave if he knew what had happened to it!

Let me close with a quotation from the Oxford physicist F. A. Lindemann.

"The recognition of the inadequacy of the old space-time coördinates has introduced a new and resilient factor into the hard and unyielding mechanism of classical physics. The harsh sequence of cause and effect has lost its power; the implacable rule of determinism its rigor. The narrow crust in which our predecessors encased our mental processes has been breached and we are entitled henceforward in the order of our physical concepts to question the grim preëminence accorded by age-long consent to *Time*."

Perhaps the Mad Hatter had a reason for calling time *Him*.

TIME
AND CHANGE
IN
HISTORY

2

TIME AND CHANGE IN HISTORY

John C. Merriam

Time has been interpreted in an almost infinite variety of ways, and no single statement can do more than picture it from one point of view. In general terms, the concept of time suggests a mirror reflecting change. According to what it is that changes, and the point of view or purpose of observation, the aspects of time will vary.

In a careful statement on this subject presented by Dr. R. A. Millikan in the James Arthur Foundation lecture of 1932, consideration was given to "time-rate-of-change of position," which is velocity, and "time-rate-of-change of velocity," which is acceleration. These were related to concepts of force as concerning uniformity of nature and natural law, and to the concept of continuity of nature or the necessary continuity of motion and change of motion.

The question presented by Dr. Millikan was discussed in terms of recent views indicating that there can be no absolute frame of reference for motion, the relative motion of two bodies alone being measurable. This formulation links space and time in a "space-time" concept. These views indicate further that velocity and position, or energy and time, are not independent of each other, and that we have no warrant for considering absolute time, as also none for considering absolute length.

In one sense what physicists have discovered is that conceptions of time and space, once assumed to hold consistently, are not really valid except under the special conditions which control in the relations specifically observed. This situation is, however, met in nearly every field of science. Often we assume broad understanding of a group of phenomena from the conditions first examined.

The concept of time, as we use it, generally seems to have limitations comparable to those suggested by present-day application through mathematics and physics. But just as the physicist, even after discussion of limitations on his views of time and space, continues to make measurements and to draw conclusions within certain limits, so in other discussions involving time-concepts, broad relations are used as basis for discussion of important questions, but with recognition of the consequences due to relative conditions.

CONCEPT OF HISTORICAL TIME

Time in the historical sense may, as has been suggested, be considered as mirroring change. Here also the difficulties of relative position and movement are encountered frequently. They are illustrated by coincident presence of stages in civilization recognized as representing widely different ages in development of man. So we may have the Stone Age culture typified at one locality and the age of applied electrical energy at another.

When we perceive visually certain remote stars we know

now that the light which makes this possible began its journey in the Age of the Dinosaurs, and that what we see as of the present really represents an earlier age. If by chance the remote suns which transmit us this light have around them planets on which the evolution of life is under way, the living things on those planets might be very different today from what they were when the light began its journey to this earth.

METHOD OF MEASUREMENT

As in other kinds of measurement, it is necessary in the problem of history to inquire as to the method of measuring and its precision. Practically all time scales that concern history refer to the same basis; namely, the period of rotation of the earth on its axis and that represented by revolution of the earth about the sun.

In any attempt to reach finality as to these standards, variation in length of day and year must be considered. From calculation by various methods it appears that small changes may have taken place, but over the ages the extent of deviation from present units of measurement seems to have been slight. Apparently such variations have had little influence upon the scheme of calculation for historical time used as a background against which to project changes in history as we visualize them.

AMOUNT OF TIME AVAILABLE

The amount of time available for what may be called history, in general terms, is also a significant matter. Written or other records consciously prepared by man cover only a few thousand years. And, important as these statements are, sometimes we admit that one of their main values is as reflection of opinion of the writers rather than as record of facts.

Unwritten history of human life presents itself in a wide variety of forms comprising remains and traces indicating life and activities for perhaps a million years. Behind this comes the record of the earth in geology, furnished by every conceivable kind of relic or imprint picturing realities of past ages.

In the sciences of the earth there is a rapidly growing body of knowledge concerning time, as corresponding to the measure of years or revolutions about the sun. Physicists and astronomers have considered the extent of the period available on the basis of limits within which the sun might have given the earth an adequate supply of light and heat. This time appeared at first probably not longer than two or three tens of millions of years. Newer views concerning nature of the sun, and solar radiation, have changed the extent from a few tens of millions to several thousand millions.

In another way the geologist, estimating time on the basis of rates of erosion and sedimentation, has built up figures requiring increasing millions, until limits originally set by physicist and astronomer have seemed inadequate for statement of what the geologist finds.

With the latest phases of study on the age of the earth, what might be called internal evidence has been much refined and extended by estimate of rates of radiation in breaking down of minerals enclosed in the rocks. So the study of uranium minerals leaving in their disintegration process a residue of lead, when checked against refined laboratory observations, gives a possible age for some of the oldest rocks of between one thousand and two thousand million years.

In the meantime the calculations of astronomer and physicist in research on life of the stars or suns have given age limits for those units, on the basis of previously unknown physical processes, suggesting a period of activity for our own sun at least as long as the age calculated for the oldest rocks in the geological record of earth history.

In such estimates as have been mentioned figures will vary greatly. For the present it is mainly mode of approach to this knowledge and order of magnitude that are of particular importance. Lectures of later years in this course will, I assume, give you, as it were, bulletins on the advance of science in this fascinating field.

The purpose of this particular lecture is mainly to direct attention toward the significance of certain aspects of change characterizing what has happened within the period of earth history as evidenced by our record. It is desired also to examine the nature of these changes and to inquire as to conclusions which may be drawn from trends of processes shown in these events, as they are measured in the rough frame of earth time.

NATURE OF HISTORICAL RECORD USED FOR
EXPRESSION OF TIME

Fragments of the actual historical record of the earth to which reference is made can be found in a thousand ways, and in nearly every region of the earth. But there are places where the story is so clearly real in all its aspects that the mind not only accepts it fully, but uses it as basis of reference for other situations less readily pictured.

Among exceptional opportunities for obtaining an impressive vision of time, the Grand Canyon of Arizona is perhaps the greatest in America, or even in the universe as we know it. Peculiar conditions have exposed an almost perfectly maintained record, and have presented it in a frame of magnitude and beauty which helps to draw instant attention and to make ineradicable imprint upon the mind. With vital reality, the vision of time reveals itself there like the opening of a door upon the past. Even more striking than the contrast of physical grandeur of the gorge with gullies and canyons we have known is the comparison of that great chasm of ages with the measure of passing years as we have fathomed them.

For those who go down into the Canyon to set their feet upon the strands of early time, represented in the rocks, these are places where history not merely reveals itself, but seems waiting to tell its story. With a sense of reality like that of the present, in standing before these ancient records of the earth, we are conscious of the streaming waters that rattled the heaps of worn and battered rocks which now form the walls, or of lapping waves as they spread upon ancient beaches the sands which are today sandstones of the bordering cliffs.

But the meaning of this record is not comprised wholly in the startling reality of the many episodes in history that one encounters, nor yet in the truth that the sequence in which we find them is the true order of changes in nature. When from some commanding point one looks out over the spectacle, not merely is there apparent the real significance of each of a multitude of incidents in their natural order, but the relation of these differing aspects of the world to each other translates them into an expression of activity extending through time. One sees the mechanism of nature and of history as if with all its parts in operation, and compasses the great complex in a single sweep of vision.

This picture represents in the truest sense an abyss in time cutting across the ages. It shows in clear perspective the reality, the sequence, and the movement in a vast tide of events.

The Grand Canyon is a magnificent spectacle merely as magnitude, or as color, or as illustration of architectural and pictorial patterns, but perhaps more than in any other way it has human value as a means of indicating what change, movement, and time are, and how they present a background for all human thought and purpose and planning. Without such an appreciation of perspective in depth or height, or of the streaming movement in the currents of change, there is little possibility of reaching even an approximation to true vision regarding great events or affairs, whether they concern nature, mankind alone, or man in the world where he is placed, or even humanity in the world which it is proceeding to make for itself.

That portion of the geological history of the earth of which we have an approximately continuous, realistic record is illustrated in a succession of strata, formed under conditions not unlike those known in the present. When pieced together these layers give us a thickness of something like forty or fifty miles of rock. This is not all found at one place, and probably represents a rate of deposition not matched precisely at any known locality. Throughout the major part of this thickness the strata differ little from accumulations being made along the borders of seas or rivers or on land at the present time, and no difficulty is experienced in appreciating the nature of the conditions which obtained when the deposits were forming.

As we approach the earlier portions of this record, increasing length of the period during which these rocks have been in existence means that we might expect increasing modifications due to the larger number of general and local movements of the earth's crust in this relatively longer time, and to the many agencies that might modify the rocks. When the lower portion of this section is reached, these influences, expressed in breaking, crushing, and intrusion by molten materials from below, so affect the rocks that their original characteristics largely disappear. In the lowest portion of the pile the formations are either materials which have passed through a molten state and, therefore, do not possess their original structure, or they have been influenced in other ways to such an extent as to produce modified mineralogical and physical characters.

So in the lowest or earliest part of the great section of the Grand Canyon the rocks through which the present lower gorge of the river is cut show evidences of change to such extent that until recently there has been doubt whether they were once sediments like those of today, or whether perhaps they owe their origin to some other process.

Regardless of astronomical calculations it would appear, then, that our earth is so old that the earliest records have been practically destroyed, and for evidences of history we must be dependent mainly upon this one thousand to two thousand million years of connected story. Within this period geological events present abundant data that indicate the nature of the earth, its structure and movements, the processes that have influenced it, and the changes that have taken place.

TIME AND PROCESS AS KNOWN FROM
GREAT BIOLOGICAL CHANGES

As an illustration of the significance of historical change taken from the field of life science, Darwin's great contribution on study of biological change or evolution was founded in part upon geological and palaeontological records, which he considered in terms of processes involved in the history of life. Darwin states in his *Voyage of the Beagle,* concerning his early work in South America:

This wonderful relationship in the same continent between the dead and the living, will, I do not doubt, hereafter throw more light on the appearance of organic beings on our earth, and their disappearance from it, than any other class of facts.

And again in his *Origin of Species:*

Judging from the past, we may safely infer that not one living species will transmit its own unaltered likeness to a distant futurity. . . . As all the living forms of life are the lineal descendants of those which lived long before the Cambrian epoch, we may feel certain that the ordinary succession by generation has never once been broken, and that no cataclysm has desolated the whole world.

The element of continuity described by Darwin is critical, in that it makes possible the process of building. Incidentally, it is this continuing relation that gives greatest dignity to human life, as through it life is fitted into a growing or developing scheme.

The theory of evolution in one form is a historical view of life. It is based on consideration of many factors, but it was seen early as a phenomenon presented in terms of change or time. It ranks among the most progressive and most comforting ideas that mankind has come to know.

CHANGE AND THE RECORD OF MAN

In the historical record of man himself, considered in its greatest extent through time, we have unequivocal evidence of changes corresponding to those known for the long sequence of other types of life preceding man. Human history finds its beginnings in a stage of geological time considerably removed from the present, and marked by conditions upon the earth materially different from those of today. Within the period of history presented, man has himself changed greatly. From what we know of history in other groups, we are led to believe that conditions governing in evolution or development of other living things in some part influenced development of man.

When we consider the record of cultures or civilizations developed by mankind we see tremendous advance in accomplishment, both material and intellectual. Both individual activity and the broader human relations have provided endless variety of contribution through experiments in education, and in economic, social, and governmental organization. Pride of present-day students in the achievements of this particular age must be tempered by recognition of values represented through what has been done in other epochs. In study of cultures and civilizations we know now that not until the history of achievement for all peoples and all times is brought together as consecutive stories shall we be in a position to judge as to ultimate values. Modern education finds itself returning to experiments of the Greeks. And the great group of religions often goes back to the savage to find a relatively safe view as to relation of man both to nature and to other men. Above all we learn that whether you call these changes steps or stages in human evolution, or whether you look upon them as representing that "vision without which the people perish," or whether it is all to be described just as "experience," they represent movement of events, underlying which there are principles of value to us, and which make the chart of history an important guide.

IMPERMANENCE

One of the most significant elements in observation of what happens in the world of things, inanimate, living, and cultural, is the seeming impossibility of permanence for anything, unless it be truth itself and the evidence of its application. Next to the laws of existence, the modes of change are among the most important aspects of being. So a poet has recognized the significance of this flow of events in the words:

> Weep not that the world changes—did it keep
> A stable, changeless state, 'twere cause indeed to weep.

Without assuming that all changes and modes of change can be reduced to anything like simple formulae, the records covering history of the earth and life, and all the movement of events which we know as history in its various phases, must be looked upon as evidence regarding the nature of the things with which we deal. Almost infinite complications make difficult an interpretation of much that we see, and we may not expect full understanding immediately; also the question as to why these things happen is one which science is commonly not in a position to answer. Many of the events will not easily resolve themselves into terms of what we call cause and effect as limited by description of the physical world. And yet it would be difficult to set aside these trains of events as wholly unrelated.

That history has value as experience, and that it suggests processes or modes of action does not therefore give it infallible prediction value. One of the most important evidences of history concerns the fact that nothing remains the same indefinitely—in other words, that history does not commonly repeat itself precisely. Situations already formulated may remain, but changing conditions bring new results. Prediction values may not be considered generally as clearly defined, but rather as indicating that certain situations have possibilities of a particular order.

Time and Change in History

Time, with the changes which it represents, gives to life and the world of things to which it is related an increased value suggesting the difference between the surface of a flat, unchanging world, and our place in a wide, deep universe of things in motion.

Now that we know the earth to be round, we look with amusement on those who conceive of living on a flat world. To them, not only is the earth different, but the heavens above must be wholly different from the universe round about us, as we see it. Equally interesting is the common absence of perspective in time, both in retrospect and prospect. To persons who lack this aspect of vision there is no element of depth, and no range within which developmental types of movement could take place.

The greatest value coming from our vision of change and time and their consequences is the idea that the world moves, and that what we do is important for coming generations. This will be true whether we build for the future, or reduce our opportunity by degenerative or destructive pleasures which waste the store of materials that the past has accumulated.

If there are laws or well-defined modes of procedure in history, is it then possible to consider whether by their use we may better existing conditions? Especially would this be desirable at a point where in practical affairs it becomes necessary to consider in one picture the entire earth and its inhabitants. The greater problems of today must be discussed not only in terms of world geography, but on the basis of world history as well. If isolation in space and time is really desired by any group, the best course is to find another planet, one that is perhaps bombproof and rayproof, and to which, across the frigid ocean of intervening space, no message may ever pass.

ON
THE LIFETIME
OF A
GALAXY

3

ON THE LIFETIME OF A GALAXY

Harlow Shapley

THE ASTRONOMER looks at the phenomenon of time from various aspects. To the practical worker in a national observatory the important time problems are its accurate determination through the observation of stars and the transmission of time signals. To the mathematical astronomer the most interesting aspects may be the relativistic space-time concept, time as a factor in a four-dimensional continuum, and its relation to fundamental concepts of physics and of philosophic thought.

There is a third phase of the time problem that is important to the general observer and interpreter—the aging process throughout the physical universe. It is this aspect of time that involves the ordinary intervals and durations. It is the time that we have in mind when speaking of the "years" of the various planets, the rotation periods of stars, the stages in the evolution of sidereal bodies. It is tied up in the concept of the age of the universe itself, and the lifetime of a galaxy; and, if we use this time concept carefully, as one detail in our attempted description of the world, we need not get tangled up with the desperate conundrums of the origin of time, or of its incomprehensible finish, or the possibility, even more appalling, of its unendingness.

That we are interested in measuring time, and in measuring ages in terms of recognized units of time, is undoubtedly the result of the accident of our birthplace. Our time thoughts are conditioned by the rotation of Planet Number 3 in the solar system. That planet, with its oceans of water and air, rotates like the others in a complete vacuum, that is, in interstellar space. Bodies moving in vacua are notoriously dependable in their motions, whether the motions are translation or rotation. It happens that our Number 3 rotates on its axis in a period of time much less than its period of revolution around its star, the sun; and this rapid rotation provides in the day an excellent unit for measuring duration.

The situation is different for some of the planets. Let us suppose, for example, that we are inhabitants on a planet that, like Mercury, forever keeps the same face toward its sun, and whose polar axis is perpendicular to the plane of the orbit. If we live on any part of the sun-lighted half of the planet (which I also assume to be without a moon) we cannot ordinarily see the stars or other planets; the sun, for a fixed observer, remains always in the same part of the sky; there are no days and nights regularly alternating; there is no month and, in fact, we are not conscious, astronomically, of intervals of time unless we are much wiser than the primates on Planet Number 3 have been in the past half million years. The philosophy of time is different. In fact, I doubt if on this slightly rearranged planet there is sufficient interest in time to justify the Arthurian lectures.

Figure 4. Some globular clusters, like Omega Centauri, contain great
numbers of variable stars pulsing with clock-like regularity

The Lifetime of a Galaxy

I call up this vision merely to emphasize how completely the rotation of our planet dominates the terrestrial time concept. The flow of time, the subdivisions of time, the complicated social and economic life that runs on daily schedule —all are conditioned by the fact that when Omnipotence created the earth he gave it a spin. Perhaps, to be more general, I should say that when the gods, with a little g, perpetrated this universe, they filled it full of rotations which all the philosophers together have been unable as yet to account for. Or, to put it still more impersonally, when our perturbed and wrought-up sun-star, or primal nebula, spewed out these lumps of mixed gasses that the Greeks later named planets, it gave them fragments of its own angular rotation.

However you put it, the spin of the earth on an axis somewhat inclined to the orbital plane gives rise to the measurement of time, by days and by seasons; and the accident of a large-sized neighboring satellite contributes the further erratic time interval of the month.

Time reckoning on the planet Mercury would be normally referred to the revolution period of eighty-eight days, for once in that interval the little planet in its elliptic orbit approaches relatively close to the sun; or it might be based on the periodic motions of the planets Venus and Earth. On the surface of the planet Venus, beneath the heavy clouds that exclude information of stars and planets, the ideas of time might be very peculiar; the rotation period is unknown, and through the clouds the sun is probably no more instructive than it is for us at the times of heavy overcast skies. The "days" on Jupiter and Saturn are less than half the length of ours. For the hypothetical inhabitants of comets and asteroids, timekeeping would be extremely various.

All these comments are intended to remind us that the concepts of time, more especially the habits of timing, as we know and use them, are exceedingly local, tainted with inherited habits of thought and enslaved by the astronomical mechanics of our particular neighborhood. I shall hope, therefore, when I speak on the subject of the lifetime of a galaxy, that my audience is as tainted and hopelessly conditioned as I am. If so, it may be able to understand me, although to the cosmic mind, to the Arcturians, we may be talking nonsense.

* * *

For hundreds of years the uniform rotation of the earth has been accepted as the best timekeeper known to man. The astronomer with his meridian circle is measuring this rotation when he observes the passage of stars across the meridian and corrects his standard clocks. But the scientist's distrust of the earth as a good pacemaker has increased through a century of study of the earth's rotation and of standard timepieces. There are irregularities of various sorts in the speed of rotation, which are brought to light through intricate study of stars, planets, sun, and moon. Some of these irregularities can be readily accounted for; they result from the tidal interaction of sun, earth, and moon. But other irregularities are not easily explained. To be sure, they are exceedingly small, measured in minute fractions of a second; but astronomical observations are precise, and modern clockmaking has achieved such high precision that we are practically at the point where we can time the earth against our best clocks rather than rate the clocks by reference to the rotating planet.

We could not expect to improve on the earth as a timekeeper if its surface were smooth, its internal structure homogeneous, or isotropic, and if it were relieved of the embarrassment of the perturbing moon and sister planets. A detached and lone wandering planet in space probably approaches perfection as a timekeeper.

In some later lecture on the Arthur Foundation it is probable that a detailed description will be given of the world's most accurate mechanical timekeeping devices, and therefore no account of them will be given here. In addition to the ordinary astronomical clocks, the timekeeping mechanisms will include oscillating crystals and, in particular, the elaborate and remarkable master-and-slave clocks of the Shortt design.

There are still other accurate methods of interval marking. For instance, the wave length of light, when very accurately determined, gives us a measure of the frequency of vibration inside atoms—vibrations that go on at the rate of a million trillion per hour. But these are impractical timekeepers at present, because the velocity of light is not as yet determined with sufficiently high precision to make the atomic vibrators more suitable, as clocks, than the rotating earth.

It has been suggested that we may resort to the use of the pulsations of giant stars in remote globular clusters as clocks.

Time and Its Mysteries

In some of these great stellar systems more than ten per cent of the brighter stars are variables, with definite periodic changes in their light. We have studied these faint, remote stars over an interval of thirty or forty years, and can assert with confidence that their periods of pulsation (generally something like twelve hours) are known with an accuracy of a hundredth, or even a thousandth of a second. But these variable stars also have inner perturbing troubles, and for reasons not yet clearly understood the pulsing stars gradually slow up, or speed ahead unaccountably; or, while holding steadily, on the average, to a highly accurate pulsation period, they may spasmodically fail, at any given outburst, to come to maximum brilliance at the predicted time.

Without further consideration of astronomical clocks, let us leave off discussing the machinery and proceed to explore a galaxy both spatially and temporally—defining, surveying, and timing one of these great cosmic units.

Since we have a galaxy of our own, the Milky Way, we may begin exploration near home. It contains, we estimate, a hundred thousand million stars, plus or minus; also star clusters, and oceans of dust and gas, which in some places lend brilliance to the astrophotographs, and in some places confuse the picture and block the more distant regions of the Milky Way, thus making uncertain our estimates of its size, structure, and total mass.

Our discoidal galactic system, the Milky Way organization, is apparently at least one hundred thousand light years in greatest diameter—that is, 6×10^{17} miles. Its thickness varies and the edges are ill defined, but perhaps we should

Figure 5. Hazards of galactic exploration—light and darkness
in the Southern Milky Way

say that the thickness is one half the extension along the Milky Way plane. Outside the bounds of this galactic system of ours (which, as we shall see later, may be a group of several normal galaxies) lie the still incompletely fathomed intergalactic spaces where the external galaxies, the spiral nebulae and their relatives, are scattered singly and in groups.

*   *   *

As we leave the Milky Way and enter extragalactic spaces, we come to a dramatic comparison of the time of man and the time of galaxies, a comparison that matches the duration of man's curiosity against cosmic durations.

Our study, we say, is chiefly of phenomena in the intergalactic spaces, far beyond the bounds of our Galaxy. But actually the external universe that we analyze, and have analyzed for the past thirty or forty years, and will continue to study for the next two or three hundred years, is in one sense not outside at all. Our information, past, present, and future, is based wholly on the radiation that comes to us from these external regions; and although this radiation is streaming along at the rate of one hundred and eighty-six thousand miles per second, we shall get, in our lifetime, the chance to examine only that small portion now rapidly converging toward this planet, that small portion which is already nearer to us than the average naked-eye star. All the hundreds of photographs we shall make within the next four years of the external galaxies which lie at the bounds of creation will be taken wholly in the light that is now nearer to us than the nearest of fixed stars. The nearest bounds of our own Galaxy are certainly more than two thousand light years distant, and therefore the light from external galaxies that we may study for the next twenty centuries is already within our galactic system.

We are with these thoughts dealing directly with cosmic perspective. And how absurd it makes our human activities appear! For example, nightly at our South African station we photograph galaxies in light that is a cool million centuries old; but once the photograph is made we hurry to rush it to the seaport and worry and fret about getting it to America and to Cambridge, where we sit and nervously examine, measure, and discuss—a rush at the finish because of the brevity of man's time allotment—amusing if not ridiculous when we compare our feverish activity and the casual flow of that radiant energy across interstellar space for the hundred million years since its release from the stars in a remote galaxy. When that radiance left the distant stellar surfaces, terrestrial mammalia were getting started in the late Mesozoic times, and as it drifted on the primitive primates were developing throughout the Miocene and Pliocene and Pleistocene periods. Still casual and unconcerned it has come during the past million years, while pre-man was struggling with his problems of food and superstition, and getting more curious about everything; on during the past two thousand years or so, until finally, after a few fleeting centuries of scientific preparation a terrestrial man pulls the slide on a plateholder and photographically captures three hours of the unending stream of energy. The three hours' exposure and the photographically absorbed radiation suddenly be-

The Lifetime of a Galaxy

come the objects of our close attention. The light has had an abundance of unreckoned time throughout the millenia in the vastness of metagalactic space; then a sudden rush and fluster at the end. What a finish! Sometimes I suspect that I know why the stars are twinkling. But why should we get man into this picture of chronological problems? The subject is the lifetime of a galaxy.

*   *   *

Galaxies are numerous in type but so far as our present records go they do not differ greatly from one another in physical properties such as total mass, total radiation, and linear dimensions. They are to be numbered by the millions, and the stellar population of each is to be placed at not much under a billion (on the average). We are able, however, to analyze closely only the few thousand galaxies that are within our neighborhood. The remoter millions are so far away that on the best of our photographs with the greatest of our telescopes the combined luminosities of their stars are registered merely as hazy indefinite patches.

The total of the system of galaxies I call the Metagalaxy; and as a convenient unit of measurement throughout metagalactic spaces we have invented the megaparsec, to use instead of miles expressed in quintillions, or light years which are units of 6×10^{12} miles. But the megaparsec, which is 3.26×10^6 light years, or about 2×10^{19} miles, is an unfamiliar term and I shall therefore use the familiar light year in the following pages.

The nearest of external galaxies, so far as we know—and we probably have the inner Metagalaxy pretty well surveyed—

is the Large Cloud of Magellan, shown in an accompanying picture. Its distance is something under a hundred thousand light years, which is so small, as extragalactic distances go, that we are able with moderate-size telescopes to resolve this neighboring galaxy into individual stars. There are only a score or two of galaxies that can be thus resolved with any kind of telescope and photographic plates at present available, and it is unlikely that the photographic and telescopic developments of the near future will add greatly to the possibilities of star-by-star analysis of external systems.

The resolvability of the Large Magellanic Cloud makes it of unusual importance. To be sure, it is only the giant and supergiant stars in that system that are bright enough for our records, but they number by the tens of thousands, and through the study of their spectra, light variation, motions, and other characteristics we are enabled to go deeply into the anatomy of such systems. Unfortunately the Large Magellanic Cloud is not a very typical external galaxy—it is irregular in form, rather than smoothly spheroidal or more typically spiral. Only two or three per cent of the external galaxies exhibit such broken and disordered structure. We must go to the ten times as distant spirals, like the great Andromeda Nebula, or Messier 33, to find the more usual form.

Much can be written about our long and intensive analyses of systems like the Large and the Small Magellanic Clouds and the Andromeda Spiral, but in the present discussion we should keep our thoughts somewhere near the conceptions of ages and time intervals. Through recent in-

Figure 6. A disordered universe—the Large Magellanic Cloud,
the nearest of external galaxies

vestigations at the Harvard Observatory it has been found that the extreme diameter of the Large Cloud of Magellan is something like twenty thousand light years. The average star in that system will take several hundred million years for an orbital circuit—an indication both of galactic space-time intervals and of the habits of stars in a galaxy. We know that if stars in such a system should travel back and forth among their neighbors a few hundred times, the distribution of stars would become smooth, and irregularities of structure disappear. We must infer, therefore, from the irregular form of the Large Magellanic Cloud either that it is not a few hundred thousand million years of age, or that it has, in relatively recent times, undergone destructive dynamical experiences that have spoiled its former symmetry and uniformity.

Scattered throughout the Magellanic Cloud, in the more or less empty spaces beyond the border of its main structure, are a considerable number of star clusters. Some are of the globular type, some are of the sparser open type, like our familiar Pleiades or Hyades. Those that lie well outside the bounds of the principal structure of the Cloud may circulate in orbits that keep them more or less free from the destructive influences of the central region. It is conceivable that an external circulating globular cluster, whether it be a member of the Magellanic Clouds or of the Andromeda Nebula (which also has such clusters), or of our own galactic system which is surrounded by a hundred globular clusters—it is conceivable that such freely moving components of an external galaxy may indefinitely withstand diffusion and losses through collisions. But the clusters that lie deeply embedded in rich fields of stars, whether like the Pleiades in our own system or like the scores of open clusters in the Large Magellanic Cloud, cannot long survive the disintegrating effects of their gravitational environment. Dr. Bok has shown that a loose grouping such as the Hyades must disintegrate beyond recognition as a star cluster after an interval of three billion years, and the much more tightly bound Pleiades could last but ten times as long.

The existence, therefore, in the Large Magellanic Cloud and in our own galactic system, of scores of open clusters is at once an indication (but not a proof) that infinite time has not been experienced by these galaxies. In fact, it strongly indicates that since the formation of galaxies probably only a few thousand million years have elapsed.

That phrase—"a few thousand million years"—has a familiar sound in science. To the layman it may seem vague and indefinite, and indicative of the inaccuracies and tentative conclusions of science. But it should be compared with other terms that have been used to indicate ages of the universe or of parts of the universe—terms like "six thousand years," "infinite time," or "ten million million years." All of these terms have been strongly advocated, the first two without the sanction of modern observational science. Perhaps we might say that the first has a theological flavor, the second metaphysical, and the third astrophysical.

The astrophysical or stellar time scale that prevailed in our hypotheses of a decade ago still has standing in science. The astronomers call it the long time scale (10^{18} years), in

The Lifetime of a Galaxy

contrast to the short time scale (10^{10} years) which has been intimated above in the discussion of the age of our galaxy and the Magellanic Cloud. The long time scale has two or three points in its favor. It is more comfortable. It does not seem to hurry the processes of evolution. The earth itself is a few thousand million years old, and there is therefore a cramped feeling when one contemplates the evolution of great stars, star clusters, galaxies, and clusters of galaxies in about the same time interval as has been used for the evolution of terrestrial organisms. But this *feeling* about the time scale should have little weight, although picturesque aesthetic preferences in such cosmogonic matters have been expressed by de Sitter, Eddington, and other leaders in the field.

The traditional views on stellar evolution, which demand processes of transformation of stellar material into stellar radiation, require the long time scale. It would take 10^{13} years for a star like Sirius to evolve into a star like the Sun. But we must remember that this word "traditional" is not very impelling; it really means the views of ten years ago. Thirty years ago the "traditional" stellar evolution hypotheses had not been invented, and the advocates of the short time scale can justifiably look for new hypotheses of the origins and lives of stars that do not involve the slow procession, through loss of mass by radiation, from one type of star to another.

As remarked above, but not explained, "a few thousand million years" is a phrase with a familiar sound. It is reminiscent of two important and clear-cut scientific deductions leading to an estimate of the time that has passed since the moment scientists define as "T = T₀." One is the age of the terrestrial rocks as determined by the measurement of the effects of radioactivity—the measurement of the amount of uranium, thorium, helium, and lead in various minerals throughout the various geological periods. Some of the most ancient rocks have been measured as about two thousand million years in age, thus giving a lower limit for the age of the earth. There is another radioactivity argument indicating that the earth cannot be more than two or three times as old. A few thousand million years ago, therefore, was an epochal time for the earth and the solar system as well as for the Large Cloud of Magellan and our own Galaxy.

The second familiar phenomenon with a definite dating is the expansion of the universe. Through frequent mention of its details, the public as well as scientists have become fully aware of the recession of external galaxies. Extensive observations show that at a distance of a million light years galaxies (whatever their direction) are receding with the speed of about seventy-five miles a second. At two million light years the speed is 150 miles a second, at ten million it is 750 miles, and so on. The observed speed of recession is proportional to the distance—at least as far out as we have measured. It is reasonable to believe that this linear relationship breaks down as the recessional speed approaches the velocity of light. But have these enormous speeds prevailed in the past? If they have existed as now, without change in quantity, about twenty-five hundred million years ago the galaxies must have all been near together. But the usual interpretation on the basis of the relativity theory suggests that the speeds are accelerated—they increase with time —and the date of the beginning of expansion is about five thousand million years ago. On either interpretation we find that the age of the expanding universe, like the age of the earth and the Galaxy, is a few thousand million years.

It should be said parenthetically that Eddington has calculated from the theory of relativity and other relevant physical theory that the speed of recession is about 150 miles per second at the distance of a million light years—about twice the observed value. I think it more likely that modification of the theory is required than that observational uncertainties are great enough to explain the wide discrepancy.[1] Hubble's earlier observed value of the rate of expansion is somewhat nearer to the calculation, but a revision of his results has been made necessary by further measures of the magnitudes of external galaxies.

* * *

The long continued expansion of the universe has scattered widely the galaxies of stars. Less than a dozen are known within a million light years of our own galactic system, and there is growing evidence that those around us constitute a local "supergalaxy." There is some evidence, indeed, that our own galactic system is itself multiple rather than a single simple spiral. Its dimensions are much larger than those of an average galaxy, and its mass of stars appears to exceed by many times the masses of even the largest galaxies. Patient investigations during the next decade of the

[1] A year after these sentences were written Eddington reëxamined the theory and found need to divide his calculated speed by two.

numbers, motions, and distances of the stars will probably resolve this difficult problem of the nature of our own galactic system. But whatever its structure, it appears to be associated with the Magellanic Clouds, the Andromeda Nebula and its two companions, and a few other near-by objects in a primitive gravitational organization of an order higher than that of a galaxy. It is probable that within this local supergalaxy there is no appreciable expansion. In this region of more than average density of matter, the cosmic repulsion does not exceed gravitational attraction.

Throughout the explored part of the Metagalaxy there are many other regions for which the number of galaxies per unit volume is higher than for space in general. Some of these relatively populous regions are supergalaxies, such as our own. Others seem to be much larger in extent, richer in membership, and provisionally we call them Metagalactic Clouds of galaxies; we see in them evidence that the distribution of matter throughout the universe is very nonuniform, and see the possibility that the speed of expansion is not everywhere the same.

It is surprising to find in the thirty or forty supergalaxies which have been investigated that the density of population does not differ much among them, though it averages something like one hundred times the population density for space in general. The present existence of these supergalaxies and metagalactic clouds appears to be another indication that the universe of galaxies is relatively young. If the time since the formation of the galaxies were 10^{13} years (the long time scale) or more, the unevennesses in distribution

The Lifetime of a Galaxy

should have been smoothed out, and these loosely organized supergalaxies should have scattered beyond recognition, because of cosmic repulsion, or collapsed into much denser groups of galaxies through the dominance of gravitation and collision.

But the use of a census of galaxies in estimating ages in the Metagalaxy should properly require much more extended investigations. The Harvard survey of the inner Metagalaxy has thus far covered but about one third of the sky, and it reaches only a hundred million light years or so into space. When this census is completed and the number of recognized galaxies is raised from the present value of about one hundred and seventy-five thousand to something like half a million, we shall have the raw material for analyses that should tell much of present structure and past behavior. From this extensive census and from the steadily increasing information on the motions of stars and galaxies we shall soon be able to affirm with weighty evidence, or to question with clear argument, our present provisional deduction that the galaxies hereabouts and the planets and the Great Expansion are all about five thousand million years from that catastrophic and creative time that astronomers call T_0.

THE BEGINNINGS

OF

TIME-MEASUREMENT

AND

THE ORIGINS

OF OUR CALENDAR

4

THE BEGINNINGS
OF TIME-MEASUREMENT AND THE
ORIGINS OF OUR CALENDAR

JAMES H. BREASTED

THE PROCESSES of matter seem to be the most tangible yard-stick which we can apply to that mysterious flow which we call time. But the processes of matter are sublimely indifferent to the insignificant time frontiers erected by man's petty scientific terminology. As if in ridicule of such barriers raised by the children of time, the operations of the universe cross and recross the tiny areas which man has staked out. We are like some frontiersman in the night holding up a torch over a dark stream and imagining that the circle of its hurrying current revealed by the torch light is all there is to the stream, while there may be Great Lakes above and a thundering Niagara below.

In this brief discussion of a vast subject let me make it clear that I am not dealing with any philosophical conceptions of time or its nature. I am merely endeavoring to present a sketch of some historical aspects of man's notions of time, by a study of the earliest sources of information available, with the purpose of disclosing especially the earliest known methods of time-measurement and the origins of our calendar.

DISCONTINUOUS TIME

Modern science has so long been dealing with time as something in *continuous* flow that we accept this conception as a matter of course. This notion of time, however, as uninterrupted duration, in ceaseless, ever-continuing flow, was the final result of ages of human effort to deal with it, and did not arise until an advanced stage of civilization. An American Indian, before he was touched by civilization, would have told you that he was "fifty winters" old, or a younger native would have said that his age was "twenty snows." He thus measured time in disconnected fragments, and throughout the globe that has been the only conception of time discernible by primitive men. Some of these time fragments are fixed seasons in the early man's folk calendar. Among certain Swedish peasants even at the present day a birthday may fall at the "rye harvest," or at the "potato harvest." A Palestinian peasant may fix the date when a note falls due, not at the end of a continuous series of months, but at the next ripening of the fakûs, a kind of cucumber. Convenient fractions of time may be designated as so many *nights.* In English we still have in common use the period "fortnight," an abbreviation of "fourteen nights." Somewhat less common is the term, "sennight," for "seven nights." This use of nights as a series of disconnected time fragments, still current in English, is of course a survival from primitive usage like our own North American Indian's measurement of a short journey to a mountain visible on the horizon as "so many sleeps." For a longer journey, however, to the sea far behind the mountain, the Indian would say "so many moons."

For ages the primitive man had no conception of time, but merely of a series of disconnected units of time, what modern investigation calls "discontinuous time." The short period during which the moon disappears is so brief that a succession of moons was not broken up into disjointed links, and a series of moons therefore gave the early man his longest uninterrupted flow of time. The moon thus became the first continuous time-measurer for periods of time within the year. Almost everywhere the primitive woman knows that ten moons (that is about nine months) after her periods have stopped her child will be born. That measurement of the length of pregnancy is one of the oldest continuous time units on record; but it fell short of a year by almost three moons. The process of linking together the disconnected time units to form a year and thus build up a calendar was an achievement belonging to an advanced stage of civilization.

THE LUNI-SOLAR YEAR

The cycle which we call a year was, of course, early observed by primitive man. The changing phases of the face of nature could not fail to attract his attention, nor could he fail to notice that certain of these phases recurred with great regularity. On some of them he was dependent for sustenance and life itself. Every day there impinged upon him some aspect of the natural world, of sky and earth in a sweepingly wide range, from the far-off celestial bodies above to the changing life below, of trees and plants, cattle and birds and insects, and the sacred observances of man himself, based to no small extent upon occurrences in the natural world. While he had noted these recurrences for ages, the early man made no effort to determine the number of days in the cycle between any one of these events and its next recurrence, and thus to establish the length of the year. Simple as it seems to us, the conception of the year, the length of its duration, and the mere arithmetic of counting the days which it occupied were far beyond human powers at first. What he did at first observe, however, was that the seasons recurred after an interval of about twelve moons. For ages his ideas of the length of year remained wholly vague as a group of roughly twelve moons. Gradually each moon month gained a name drawn from some event in the life of plants and animals, or some sacred observance of man himself connected with such an occurrence in nature.

The effort to fit the series of moon months into the cycle of the year was never successful. Throughout the ancient world, especially in Western Asia and Greece, man struggled with the practical problem of the incommensurability of the length of the year and the moon month. We are accustomed to say that the Greeks were the first people to gain complete intellectual emancipation, but in the measurement of time their men of science suffered under such complete intellectual subjection to inherited tradition in the use of the moon month as a subdivision of the year that they continued to use a year divided into months of which there were twelve and a fraction in each year. They resorted to elaborate devices for making a term of years equal to a given number of integral moon months. They devised a cycle of eight years with three intercalated moon months, or more accurately, of nineteen years with seven intercalated moon months. The engineer Meton, who adopted the nineteen-year cycle from acquaintance with Babylonian astronomy, knew well enough that his elaborate cyclic scheme did not match exactly with the observed New Moons. In view of this fact it is most extraordinary that the Greeks never possessed the intellectual emancipation to reject the moon entirely from their calendar and adopt a conventional month dictated by social needs. They knew of the Egyptian calendar, and in the middle of the fifth century B.C. Herodotus praises it, evidently under the impression that its year of 365 days was correct. But the Greeks had inherited their lunar calendar from Babylonia, and it was so firmly entrenched in their life, beliefs, and customs that they were never able to cast it off.

From the earliest times the lunar month dominated the calendar of Western Asia, where it arose at least as early as the fourth millennium B.C. under the leadership of Babylonian civilization. The Babylonian kings at first adopted an erratic method of intercalated months inserted at irregular intervals, by royal command whenever the king noticed, as Hammurabi says in one of his letters, that "the year hath a deficiency." He then ordered the insertion of an intercalary month. It was not until 528 B.C. under Persian sovereignty that Babylonia adopted a fixed lunar cycle for the insertion of intercalated months at regular intervals. It was this cyclic system which was introduced from Babylonia by the Greeks. At the very time when the Greeks were thus fastening upon themselves the intolerable inconvenience of a lunar calendar they might have observed that Darius the Great, the ablest administrator of the Ancient World, had introduced into the Persian Empire the Egyptian calendar, which disregarded the moon month. The long established habits of the Western Asiatic peoples, however, and especially the eventual triumph of Islam, resulted in the universal restoration of the lunar calendar. The disharmony between the lunar and the solar year was carried to the absurdest conceivable extreme by Mohammed, who was so densely ignorant of the nature of the calendrical problem that in the Koran he actually forbade the insertion of intercalary months. The so-called "lunar year" of 354 days, being eleven days shorter than the solar year, revolves entirely around the solar year in a little over thirty-three years, that is, about three times in every century. A monthly observance like Ramadhân, the month of fasting, if it is now in June, will be in April six years from now. It is now (1935) 1,313 years since the Hijra, or the Hegira, the beginning of the Moslem era, but each of our centuries contains over 103 of the shorter Moslem lunar years. In 1,313 of our Gregorian years there are about forty-one more Moslem years, so that the Moslem era of the Hijra is now in the year 1354 (that is, 1,313 plus forty-one).

The authorities of the Jewish church in the Orient avoided such absurdity, and employed intercalation to keep their lunar calendar at least roughly within the framework of the solar year. All Western Asia therefore still continues to suffer under the inconvenience of the most primitive form of time-measurement, the lunar calendar.

THE STELLAR YEAR

The Egyptians were the only ancient people who clearly recognized the cause of that inconvenience and possessed the courage and intellectual freedom to remove it. The total incommensurability of the solar or stellar year and the so-called "lunar year" could be discovered only after determination of the length of the solar or stellar year, and recognition of the fact that there is no such thing as a "lunar year."

The determination of the length of the year, together with the discovery that it had a fixed length, was a long slow process lying far back in prehistoric ages. As we shall see, it is an extraordinary fact that it was not the sun which first furnished early man with the length of the year. Other natural phenomena much more intimately within his circle of observation must first have revealed to him the beginning of another annual cycle. The beginning of the annual run of salmon, the blossoming of certain plants, or, after the introduction of agriculture, the successive tasks of cultivation might mark the years. The peasants of Palestine call the years so many "threshing floors"; the Arabs of Lower Iraq count the years by "date harvests"; in the East Indian Archipelago the years are counted by "rice harvests." The conception of a year thus arose gradually. On the East Indian Island of Bali the two monsoon seasons are each made up of a list of months which have the same names and are therefore identical for the two halves of the year. This fact shows us that the two seasons were separated from each other and the conception of the complete year cycle had not yet arisen. The process of uniting the seasons into a year was therefore a slow and gradual one. At first, as may still be observed among some surviving primitive peoples, there arose a list of moon months which did not fill the entire year. After those months were past, before the beginning of a new year, there followed a period of indifferent length, completing the old year. This intermediate period of varying and indifferent length served to adjust the inequality between the solar year and any number of integral lunar months, and brought the months into rough correspondence with the solar year. Eventually there arose a list of lunar months, twelve to thirteen in number, which were thought to fill the entire year. There is, however, no equivalence between an arbitrary series of lunar months and a solar or stellar year. Hence there really is no such thing as a "lunar year," and Mohammed's year of 354 days is a creation which corresponds to nothing in nature. Historically the lunar month has been useful as first suggesting a convenient series of twelve subdivisions of the year, but beyond that fact it has caused endless confusion and complication throughout human history.

The lunar month of course contributed nothing to the determination of the length of the year, and curiously enough the sun, the other great luminary, did not first enable man to discover the year and determine its length.

Beginnings of Time-Measurement

While the sun's apparent revolutions shift their positions from season to season they nevertheless go on in an unbroken series with no beginning and no end. The sun's apparent motions therefore did not at first suggest the year cycle. It is quite evident that primitive men had very early begun to observe the stars and to notice the reappearance of a prominent star or group of stars after it had been invisible for a time. Such a reappearance was an event which cut sharply into the sequence of events in the stellar sky, and easily came to mark the beginning of the year. In several regions of South America the word for Pleiades is the same as the word for year. In the eighth century B.C. Hesiod places his agricultural program in the calendar by observing the return of the Pleiades in May. If the Greeks had only continued to build up their calendar on this stellar observation, they might have saved themselves centuries of difficulty and complication with their inherited Babylonian lunar calendar.

In prehistoric ages, many thousands of years ago, the dwellers along the Nile, the greatest river known to ancient man, very naturally began their year with the beginning of the annual rise of the vast river, as the most important terrestrial phenomenon of which they knew and also the source of fertility on which an agricultural people depended for their very life. The four-month season of the inundation, which fructified the fields, was followed by another four-month season of planting and cultivation, and a third and final four-month season of harvest. This year of three four-month seasons was obviously one which arose out of the life

[67]

of an agricultural people. It was essentially an agricultural folk calendar, and its months were obviously moon-months in the beginning and doubtless continued to be so for thousands of years.

But, like primitive man everywhere, these earliest known agricultural peasants along the Nile had begun at a very remote date to scan the heavens and observe the stars, probably some thousands of years before Hesiod was doing the same in the eighth century B.C. There is probably no other country in which Sirius, the Dog Star, the brightest of the so-called fixed stars, is such a brilliant and noticeable spectacle in the evening sky. In the latitude of Lower Egypt Sirius rises about four minutes earlier every day. Every fifteen days he rises about an hour earlier, so that eventually he rises in full daylight, when he is of course entirely invisible. After a period of some months of invisibility, this brilliant and beautiful star suddenly reappears on the eastern horizon at sunrise. This "heliacal" rising of Sirius, as it is called, is a noticeable and sharply defined event. By a remarkable coincidence this heliacal rising occurs very near the time of the beginning of the inundation. In antiquity this date was the nineteenth of July. By a lucky accident, the beginning of the year at the advent of the inundation in the enormously ancient peasant calendar was thus fixed at the moment of an important astronomical event. The basis of the calendar which was to become that of the civilized world was, therefore, a stellar not a solar year.

Beginnings of Time-Measurement

THE 360-DAY YEAR

It is important to notice that the earliest observances of the heliacal rising of Sirius must have been very primitive in character, as we shall later illustrate. Persistent dust storms, such as we experience today, desert fogs and mists, or sometimes storm clouds, must have made the determination of the exact day when Sirius reappeared on the eastern horizon not a little uncertain. It is certain that the length of the stellar year as measured by successive sunrise reappearances of Sirius was at first roughly established by the Egyptians as 360 days. As early as the fourth millennium B.C., that is, well back of 3000 B.C., we find this 360-day year divided into thirty-six decads of ten days each, for grouping the constellations along the celestial equator. This appearance of a circle of thirty-six decads in the fourth millennium B.C. is highly significant. It is certainly the oldest appearance of a circle of 360 divisions. The Sumerian sexagesimal system, in which sixty appears as a numerical unit (called šuššu), is without doubt enormously old; and in all probability arose from the length of the year—360 days—by dividing it into six parts. It seems probable, as concluded by Zimmern, that šuššu, the Babylonian word for sixty, means "one sixth." In both Babylonia and Egypt the convenient and basic number (360), of fundamental importance in the division of the circle and therefore in geography, astronomy, and time-measurement, had its origin in the number of days in the year in the earliest known form of the calendar. While its use seems to be older in Egypt than in Babylonia, there is no way to determine with certainty that we owe it exclusively to either of these two countries. A common origin older than either is possible.

THE 365-DAY YEAR

The Egyptians found their primitive 360-day year very convenient in business and social life, and it therefore survived far down into the historic age; but as their observations of the heliacal rising of Sirius accumulated, they finally discovered that the year, as they thought, contained 365 days. We are in a position to determine the date when they took administrative action to make this discovery of the approximate length of the year practically effective. In the year 4236 B.C., as determined by Borchardt, some now unknown ruler of prehistoric Egypt, without doubt residing in Heliopolis, introduced a calendar year of 365 days. It began with the heliacal rising of Sirius, that is on the nineteenth of July. This calendar contained the three old agricultural peasant seasons: the inundation, the cultivation, and the harvest, each season containing four months. The epoch-making importance of this calendar lies in the fact that these twelve months were entirely divorced from any connection with the moon, so that the deviser of the calendar could make each month thirty days long. By the addition of five feast days at the end of the year, this year of twelve thirty-day months or 360 days became the earliest known and practically convenient calendar of 365 days.

Beginnings of Time-Measurement

The only celestial phenomenon to which any attention was paid in devising this calendar was the establishment of the beginning of the year at the first heliacal rising of Sirius. In other words the mind that devised this calendar put social and economic needs first and divorced the calendar from celestial processes. It is of the greatest interest to observe that this calendar inevitably soon parted company with Sirius, for, owing to the fact that the stellar year is about a quarter of a day longer than 365 days, Sirius rose a day late every four years; that is, at the end of the fourth year after the introduction of the calendar he rose on the second day of the New Year or one day late; at the end of eight years two days late; that is, on the third day of the year; at the end of twelve years three days late; that is, on the fourth day of the year; and so on to the end of the year. The calendar-makers did not at first observe this discrepancy, and when they finally did become aware of it, they held to the supremacy of social considerations, and made no attempt to shift the calendar back into harmony with Sirius. Eventually, therefore, in four times 365 years, that is, in approximately 1,460 years, the Egyptian calendar revolved entirely around the celestial year. A remark by Censorinus informs us that in A.D. 139 Sirius rose on New Year's day; that is, New Year's day in the civil calendar of Egypt once more coincided with the heliacal rising of Sirius. Borchardt has computed from astronomical calculations that the next earlier coincidence of this kind must have occurred in 1318 B.C., the next

earlier in 2776, and a still earlier one in 4236 B.C. Archaeo-
logical considerations forbid us to suppose that we may push
back still another such period of 1,460 years. We may therefore conclude that the civil calendar of Egypt was introduced in 4236 B.C.[1]

This date, near the middle of the forty-third century
B.C., is not only the earliest fixed date in history, but also
the earliest date in the intellectual history of mankind. It
has been well said that "the Egyptian calendar is the greatest intellectual fact in the history of time-reckoning."[2] but
it is far more than that. For the introduction of this calendar
was an intellectual feat, marking the dawn of a recognition
of the supremacy of social requirements. As we have already
remarked above, in divorcing this new calendar from the
processes of nature, the Egyptians were recognizing for the
first time a world of social needs which they placed first.
It is today the earliest known such recognition, and the earliest dated intellectual event in human history. It ushered
in the great epoch, which was in full development after 4000
B.C., when the Egyptians discerned that their once purely
nature-gods, who had originally been only personifications
of natural forces and natural phenomena, like the Sun-god
Re, or the Vegetation-god Osiris, were gradually shifted from
a world of natural processes to be arbiters in a newly discerned social arena, where moral forces were emerging. The

[1]The date 4241 B.C., formerly calculated for this event, contained a
small error in the factors used. After this error is corrected, the calculation gives 4236 B.C. as the correct year.

[2]Martin Persson Nilsson, *Primitive Time-Reckoning* (Lund, Sweden:
C. W. K. Gleerup, 1920), p. 280.

calendar was thus the beginning of a great movement in human life which carried over the thought of man from the world of nature to the world of human life.

EGYPTIAN SOURCE OF EUROPEAN CALENDAR

This remarkable calendar remained the exclusive possession of the Egyptians for over thirty-five hundred years after its introduction. The effort of Darius the Great to introduce it into Western Asia late in the sixth century B.C. proved unsuccessful. The Greeks, as we have seen, wasted their scientific gifts in adding one futile refinement after another to the hopelessly inconvenient and complicated Babylonian lunar calendar. Nearly four and a half centuries after the fruitless attempt of Darius, another great administrative genius gave Europe for the first time a sane calendar. In 46 B.C. Julius Caesar introduced into the Roman Empire the Egyptian calendar, with one important modification. He provided for the addition of one day to the year of 365 days once in every four years. The history of this important innovation is interesting.

The first knowledge of a year of 365 days was brought to Europe by Thales, the Ionian philosopher, who learned of it on a visit in Egypt. Curiously enough Herodotus also learned of it there and praises it as a perfect solution of the complications due to the incommensurability of moon-month and year. Neither Thales nor Herodotus seems to have known that the year of 365 days was too short. It is obvious that the Egyptians early observed the rate at which the heliacal rise of Sirius diverged from the beginning of the calendar in their civil year, revealing to them that their 365-day year was a quarter of a day short. The extraordinary achievements of the Babylonian astronomers in the Chaldean and Persian periods included a computation of the length of the solar year by Nabu-rimannu, or Naburianos, as the Greeks called him. Not long before 500 B.C. this great astronomer calculated the length of the solar year as 365 days, six hours, fifteen minutes, and forty-one seconds— a result which is only twenty-six minutes and fifty-five seconds too long. This is the earliest known close approximation to the length of the solar year.

For over a century and a half no one seems to have made any practical application of this new knowledge. It was not until the third century B.C. that the Egyptians made an effort to correct the error in the length of the year. We still possess the granite stela of Ptolemy Euergetes I, bearing his decree, dated in the year 238 B.C., which commanded that every fourth year should be one of 366 days. But the Egyptian people obstinately refused to conform to this decree, and the correction in the calendar never became effective.

In 380 B.C. the able Greek astronomer and mathematician Eudoxus visited Egypt and there learned the fact that the year was really about 365¼ days long. Then for the first time this fact became common knowledge in Europe. Some two centuries later, that is, early in the second century B.C., the great Greek astronomer Hipparchus announced that 365¼ days was in error, that is, it was too long, by one three-hundredth of a day. This error was unknown to Caesar, and we all know that for this reason in March 1582 the Julian calendar was superseded by that of Pope Gregory XIII.

It is evident, however, that Julius Caesar brought to Europe for the first time a sane calendar system of twelve thirty-day months. If jealous Roman emperors and other scientifically ignorant meddlers had not utterly disfigured the Egyptian calendar, we would not be calling the ninth month September (with the numeral seven), the tenth month October (with the numeral eight), the eleventh month November (with the numeral nine), and the twelfth month December (with the numeral ten)! Nor would our young people be obliged to learn and repeat a verse of poetry in order to find out how many days there are in a month.

THE WEEK

With the introduction of the Egyptian calendar time became something in which *human* processes were, so to say, systematically staked off into annual stages and sub-stages. These subdivisions of a calendar, particularly the shorter ones, arise only at an advanced stage of social development. The origin of the month was of course due to a celestial phenomenon, but that of the week was in origin purely human and social. A market week of three, four, five, six, eight, and ten days is a calendar division of purely secular origin. It is found over practically the entire globe, where civilization has advanced sufficiently to possess arts and crafts, with exchange and commerce of a primitive kind. It has quite commonly a rest day on which work is forbidden. There is a universal connection between rest day and religion. Among some peoples, as among the Hebrews, the religious significance of the day predominates, and the feature of rest becomes a religious mandate. For our subject, the week, whatever its origin or significance, is of slight importance, for the week has played practically no part in time-measurement.

THE DAY

For many reasons, which are too obvious to need enumeration, the smaller subdivision, the day, has always been of fundamental importance in the measurement of time. It is extraordinary that among the various peoples there should be such wide diversity in the understanding of just what a day is. Modern astronomers consider a day as beginning at midday and therefore lasting from midday to midday. The peoples having a lunar calendar conceive the day as lasting from evening to evening; while in modern life the day begins at midnight and lasts from midnight to midnight, a point of practical convenience as marking the transition from one day to the next, and ignoring the night. This conception of a twenty-four-hour day is not even yet in our railroad timetables. We really have two periods of twelve hours each, very inconveniently distinguished in our timetables by leaded or black-faced type suggesting darkness at midday, which we sagaciously shift to light-faced type, suggesting daylight at midnight! The modern languages possess no word for the twenty-four-hour day. Only the ancient Greeks seem to have possessed such a word in their convenient νυχθήμερον. The Egyptians began the day at dawn, which seems the natural thing for an originally peasant people to do. The practice of beginning the day at dawn was adopted by Europe at an early date, and continued down into medieval times. It was the introduction of the striking clock in the fourteenth century of our era that shifted the beginning of the day to midnight.

There was as much diversity in the length of the day as in the time of its beginning. In view of the varying length of the *daylight*-day no one finds anything strange about a flexible or elastic day. It is in the subdivisions of the day that we have come to expect constant length. Division of the day into hours is unknown to primitive peoples. The Greeks and Romans in the West and the Chinese in the East had originally no hour divisions of the day, which they all received from the Near East. The Greeks were accustomed to identify times of day by such cumbrous devices as "the time of full market," which was the middle of the forenoon. Subdivision of the daylight-day into twelve parts was introduced into Egyptian life at a very early date. We find it in the Pyramid Texts, and this means that it was practised in the fourth millennium B.C.; that is, before 3000 and possibly as early as 3500 B.C. The Egyptian was interested in a convenient division of his day into twelve parts, but he was not concerned that these twelve parts should be of constant length. The reason for this probably lay in his early timepieces, as we shall see. The Babylonians also possessed a subdivision of the day at an early date, but it divided the daylight-day into six parts, and the night into six more. The modern habit of translating the Babylonian term *bêru* (formerly read *kasbu*) for this part by "double hour" is of course very misleading, if not entirely incorrect.

Time and Its Mysteries

THE EARLIEST TIMEPIECES: SUN CLOCKS

What type of time-measuring devices the Egyptians at first employed we do not know. The earliest such devices that have survived in Egypt date from the fifteenth century B.C. They were of two kinds and measured time either by the observation of celestial processes, or by the employment of physical processes under artificially arranged terrestrial conditions. The celestial processes employed for time-measurement were the movements of the sun and the stars. In a country as nearly cloudless as Egypt the observation of the sun was a valuable means of determining time. The Egyptians therefore devised the earliest known sun clock.[1] In its oldest form it was an instrument shaped like a T-square laid down horizontally. The crosshead of the T-square was laid toward the East in the forenoon, and was sufficiently thick to form a barrier casting a shadow along the much longer stem, which was graduated with marks for six hours. At dawn the shadow of the crosshead cast westward by the sun just clearing the eastern horizon covered the whole length of the graduated scale out to the mark of the first hour at the end. As the sun climbed the eastern sky the shadow shortened until at noon it disappeared at the mark of the sixth hour. The instrument was then turned around with the crosshead of the T-square toward the West so that the lengthening shadow cast by the afternoon sun marched back along the hour marks to the twelfth, identical with the first hour at the end of the scale.

[1]The reader is referred to Dr. Millikan's lecture for an illustration of a sun clock, facing page 8.

Beginnings of Time-Measurement

Such a system of determining time by measuring the length of the shadow cast by the sun was of course continually subject to alteration caused by the seasonal changes in the position of the sun. At first these Egyptian sun clocks were fitted to the length of the day at the equinoxes and were not correct at any other season. It would have required some generations of experience in instrument making to have enabled even the supreme skill of the Egyptian craftsmen to produce a shadow clock of this type that would have indicated correct time.

The sun-clock makers tried to adapt their instruments to seasonal changes by using a *series* of hour scales, eventually seven in number. This showed progress and improvement; but such a sun clock was not an accurate timepiece.

Moreover the Egyptian did not yet know enough of the motions of the earth and sun nor of the mathematics involved to discern the underlying principles that should have governed the construction of his sun clock, and especially the arrangement of the hour scale for the different times of day and for the changing seasons of the year. He further improved his clock by employing only a narrow beam of sunlight and shortening the graduated scale by raising it to an oblique angle of some forty-five degrees above horizontal. While improving the accuracy of the device, these changes also made it small enough to be portable. It was indeed the earliest known portable timepiece. It was equipped with a plummet so that it might be kept in the plane of the horizon; but little could be claimed for its accuracy. The great Egyptian conqueror Thutmose III refers to the hour indicated by the sun's shadow at a critical moment while on his first campaign in Asia. It must have been, therefore, that he carried with him into Asia some form of sun clock. It is probably only a coincidence that the oldest sun clock we possess bears the name of this king.

Another form of sun clock employed the *direction* of the sun's shadow, rather than its length. Lines diverging from a center were marked on a plane surface, which might be either vertical or horizontal, and these enabled the observer to determine the different hours, which were marked next to the lines. This form of instrument was simply a sundial, and evidently the ancestor of our own sundials. Again the Egyptian makers did not understand the rather complicated problems involved in making such a device indicate time accurately. It is interesting to note that one of these Egyptian sundials[1] bearing the name of the Pharaoh Merneptah of the thirteenth century B.C. has been discovered in Palestine.

THE EARLIEST TIMEPIECES: STELLAR CLOCKS

We have seen that the Egyptians began their year by stellar observation. They must have begun very early the determination of the hour also by observation of the stars. The word "hour" was written in hieroglyphics in the earlier period of Egyptian writing, with a star after it as the so-called "determinative." In order to use the night sky as a stellar clock it was necessary that the observer should build

[1]Facing page 6 of Dr. Millikan's lecture will be found an illustration of this sundial.

up a list of important stars, together with the times at which they crossed his meridian at different seasons of the year. If complete for all the seasons, such a list would enable the Egyptian at any time of year to observe the night sky and determine the hour. He seems to have devised a primitive type of "transit instrument" intended to enable an observer to determine the instant when a given star crossed his meridian. Naïvely simple and undeveloped, this instrument was employed as the observer sat cross-legged on the flat roof of a building, supposably often a temple. Opposite him at the other end of the building squatted his assistant facing him, and both of them exactly on the same meridian which was probably marked on the roof. We know that the Egyptian engineers and surveyors of five thousand years ago could lay down a meridian with a good deal of accuracy. The oldest pyramid, that of King Snefru at Medum, was oriented in the thirtieth century B.C. with surprising accuracy. Our astronomical observer, seated on a meridian line which we may regard as fairly accurate, peeped through the forked top of a palm branch which he held in his hand as a kind of sighting staff, and sighted through the slot in the top of the palm branch at the stars in the opposite (northern) sky over the head of the squatting assistant. A star rising to culmination over the assistant's "crown," that is, the exact center of his head, might be over his "left eye," over his "left ear," or over his "left shoulder." These positions were determined with some precision by the use of a plummet. As the observer looked through the slot in his sighting staff, he held his plummet well out in front of the staff, so that the plumb-line at a point near its top cut through the star he was observing, and at a lower point just above the weight the plumb-line also cut through some part of the head or figure of the observer's assistant squatting at the other end of the building. The plumb-line then cut through one shoulder, one eye, or one ear of the assistant. Thereupon the observer could wait until, as he followed the star with his plumb-line past the ear and the eye, the plumb-line finally cut through the top or crown of the head. The star was then in culmination and was crossing the observer's meridian. This was the most important function of the device. It was chiefly a transit instrument and as such is the oldest known astronomical instrument. It was called in Egyptian a $mrh \cdot t$ or *merkhet*, meaning "instrument for knowing," to which we should add the word "hour." As an "instrument for knowing the hour" is of course a timepiece, we may regard *merkhet* as the earliest known word for "clock."[2]

It is obvious, as Borchardt has observed, that these meridian observations themselves would necessarily have had to be accompanied by some kind of time record such as is furnished today by the astronomer's clock. He has supposed that the Egyptian observer originally compiled a timetable of hours when important stars crossed his meridian, or occu-

[2] In the museum of the Oriental Institute at the University of Chicago there is a *merkhet* made by the Egyptian pharaoh Tutenkhamon. This piece was found by the writer in a London antiquity shop in 1923. The instrument bears an inscription saying that it had been made by Tutenkhamon for his ancestor Thutmose IV. It had, therefore, probably been taken at some time from the tomb of Thutmose IV in Egypt, and after three thousand years had come into the possession of an antiquity dealer in London.

pied definable positions near it, which could be stated in terms of the head and shoulders of the observer's squatting vis-à-vis. Two such star-tables have been preserved, pictured in the tombs of Ramses VI and Ramses IX at Luxor; that is, about 1150 and 1120 B.C. The positions of the stars are given at twenty-four different times of the year, that is, twice a month: on the first and the fifteenth. These tables very much need detailed study by an experienced astronomer. Thus far the only star identifiable is Sirius, and his only determinable position is his culmination. These position-tables must have been accompanied by timetables, probably on papyrus, which now seem to have perished.

THE EARLIEST TIMEPIECES: WATER CLOCKS

Evidently some kind of timepiece was employed in the compilation of these timetables, otherwise the culminations observed would not have furnished any indications of time. Borchardt has demonstrated that the Egyptian water clock, the famous clepsydra, or "water-stealer," as the Greeks called it, was used for measurement of the hours of the *night* and has therefore concluded, with much probability, that it was a clepsydra which was used to furnish the time data which transformed the night sky for the Egyptian into a vast stellar clock.

There were two types of the clepsydra, one which we may call an *outflow* clock, and the other an *inflow* clock, according as the water flowed out of, or into, the graduated vessel serving as the clock. In both these forms of clock the principle was essentially the same. Of the inflow type, which seems to have been the more accurate system, only two specimens are known to me. Thirteen examples of the outflow type have been preserved in whole or in part. The oldest of them bears the name of Amenhotep III, and therefore dates from around 1400 B.C.[1] We know, however, of a maker of such clocks, who lived a hundred and fifty years earlier, about 1550 B.C. This man, whose name was Amenemhet, is the earliest known astronomer, physicist, and clockmaker in the history of science. He left a brief autobiography engraved on the wall of his tomb-chapel in the great cemetery of Egyptian Thebes, which lies opposite modern Luxor. Amenemhet proudly tells us that he lived and served at the court of the first three Pharaohs of the Eighteenth Dynasty. He takes evident satisfaction in relating that he made a clock for Amenhotep I, that is, some time in the middle of the sixteenth century B.C. He avers that he had read all the existent literature on the subject, as a modern scientist might do. Whether in the course of this reading, or as a result of his own researches, does not appear, but our clockmaker tells us of his observation that the winter night was fourteen hours long, while the night of the harvest season (summer) was twelve hours long. He mentions that he constructed his clock in accordance with the fact that he had noted an increase in the length of the nights from month to month and also a decrease from month to month. He then goes on to say: "I made a clock ($mr\underline{h}y \cdot t$) computed for the year . . . . . [it was correct(?)] at the going in of the harvest season (summer) in the cultivation season (winter), at the

[1]See the illustration facing page 12 of Dr. Millikan's lecture.

union (?) of the moon with its seasons. Every hour was at its time."

Externally this clock, built by Amenemhet for the king of Egypt, was of unique interest, for it was the earliest time-piece of which we have any record, fitted with tiny statuette figures so devised that they appeared at the proper intervals and indicated the hours. Unfortunately, the text of Amen-emhet's autobiography is much damaged and very fragmen-tary. His description of these mechanical arrangements informs us that "Nekhbet (the Moon-goddess) walked at the same time with Re (the Sun-god) [while she extended the symbols of life and prosperity] which were in her hand, to the nostrils of his majesty. Then she went down (mean-ing she dropped out of sight) . . . . ," and unfortunately at this point there is a bad gap in the text, after which we find the words: "[and Re] rejoiced when he saw these goddesses ascending and descending before him." As Sethe has no-ticed, "these goddesses" are obviously the well-known hour-goddesses, each personifying an hour. Amenemhet had evi-dently arranged small figures of these goddesses, each of whom came into view at the proper point of time, thus by her appearance announcing the hour. It must be borne in mind that these figures belonged to a water clock and not to a mechanical clock of cogwheels and gears, for such mechanical developments were devices entirely unknown in the sixteenth century B.C. They did not come in until the Hellenistic Age, after Alexander the Great. We may sup-pose, with some probability, judging from the verbs of motion employed in the description, that the moving figures were attached to floats on the surface of the water in the clock, and that they therefore moved up and down with the changing level of the water. It must have been a pleasing and picturesque timepiece which Amenemhet devised, and he tells us with evident satisfaction that it pleased the king. It was the earliest of those ingenious and artistic mechanical clocks which the later Arabic writers describe in such detail; especially famous is that one reputed to have been sent by Harun al-Raschid to Charlemagne in the ninth century A.D.

Amenemhet's fragmentary description of his elaborate clock, combined with all the data now observable from an examination of the surviving Egyptian water clocks, especially the oldest of the outflow clocks, does not reassure us regarding our ancient astronomer's ability to construct an accurate timepiece. In the simplest terms this device consisted of a water vessel, with a hole in or near the bottom for the escape of the water and a graduated scale of hours engraved on the inside from the top to a point near the bottom.[1] The outflow clocks were in the shape of inverted truncated cones; the inflow clocks were usually cylindrical. There were many inflow water clocks used in Roman times, but the outflow clocks were probably more common among the ancient Egyptians.

THE HOUR

Now the function of such a clock was to divide the night into twelve equal parts. There was, however, no sufficient

[1]An illustration of the outflow clock will be found in Dr. Millikan's lecture, facing page 12.

method for securing a uniform flow of water during each one of these twelve parts. The hours decrease too rapidly in length from the beginning to the end of the scale of hour marks on the inside of the vessel. Only in the middle is one hour that is approximately correct. Amenemhet indicates that his clock was adjusted to show the hours for all seasons of the year. His narrative, as well as the surviving water clocks, show that whether the night was short or long, it continued to be divided into twelve periods, that is to say, in winter each of the twelve periods of the night was longer, and during the nights of summer each of the twelve periods was shorter. In other words, the hours were not of constant length. We are accustomed to a flexible day of varying length, but an hour of elastic length is surprising to us. The scheme of marks was intended to indicate the lengths of the nights in all the different seasons. Indeed the later water clocks provide for indicating a change in the length of every night, from night to night, and in the period around 300 B.C. these indications were essentially correct.

THE HOUR AND THE TWENTY-FOUR-HOUR DAY

The twenty-four-hour day, with hours of variable length, longer in the winter nights and shorter in the summer nights, or longer in the summer days, and shorter in the winter days, reached Greece probably with the Egyptian clocks in the time of Alexander the Great. We know that an Egyptian clock was shown to the cynic Diogenes as something unusual and curious. It passed thence to Rome, where the first sun clock appeared in 293 B.C., having come into

Italy by way of the Greek cities of Sicily. The first water clock did not arrive in Rome until 159 B.C. It is important to notice that the Greeks and Romans both had small divisions of the day long before this. Homer knew of divisions of the night determined by observation of the constellations, and Herodotus tells of Babylonian devices for determining divisions of the day. An interesting evidence of the twelve-hour day in Greece is to be found in a passage from Aristotle as quoted by the scholiast on the Iliad. Here Aristotle refers to the "twelve parts of the night" (τῆς νυχτὸς αἱ δώδεκα μοῖραι).

The Egyptian hour of varying length, which thus came into Europe with the twenty-four-hour day, remained in use nearly down to the end of the Middle Ages. The Babylonian *bêru* (formerly *kasbu*), a period of one sixth of day or night, was of fixed length, and may eventually have had some influence on the European hour; but the hour of fixed length did not come into general use in Europe until the fourteenth century of our era, when it was introduced by the striking clock which inevitably gave it wide currency.

SUBDIVISION OF THE HOUR

We have already seen that primitive life did not possess the subdivision of the day into hours. Much less did it have any shorter divisions of time. There are of course inexact terms of no fixed significance, as we say, "the twinkling of an eye," or the German *Augenblick*. For a vague period of about half an hour, the natives of Madagascar say "a rice-cooking," while for a moment they say "the frying of a locust." The Cross River natives say "a complete maize-roasting" for something less than a quarter of an hour. In Illinois when I was a lad, a farm hand would facetiously indicate a moment by the phrase, "two jerks of a lamb's tail." The shortest interval of time indicated by the Egyptian was written in hieroglyphics simply by the upraised head of a hippopotamus, with a horizontal line cutting it off. This line was intended to represent the surface of the water, and the idea suggested was that of the instant of time during which the hippo cautiously thrust his head out of the water for a quick glance around and its almost instantaneous disappearance. That was the Egyptian scribe's ingenious writing of the word "instant"; but this word did not indicate a subdivision of the hour. Insofar as we can discern, the hour was divided in early Christian times in Egypt into the half, the quarter, the eighth, etc. The sexagesimal subdivisions of the hour into minutes and seconds, now customary with us, are not earlier in the Orient than about A.D. 1000, and they did not appear in the Western World until the end of the Middle Ages. The source of these divisions is unknown, but it has been suspected with some probability that the Arabic astronomers applied them to the hour from the use of them in dividing the circle, in which connection they are likewise not of early Oriental origin. Even Ptolemy did not divide the circle into sexagesimal degrees, although he did apply the sexagesimal divisions to the radius of his circle.

There are indications of a small division of time employed by the Egyptian surgeons at an early date (nearly five thousand years ago) for the counting of the human pulse, and it is known that Hippocrates some twenty-five centuries later was already counting the pulse. Obviously some subdivision of the hour, and some timepiece for measuring it, must have been used for this purpose. The surprisingly accurate determinations of the length of the planetary revolutions by the Chaldean astronomers must have required timepieces adapted for use in measuring fractions of time smaller than the hour. No examples of Babylonian timepieces have survived, however, and the whole matter awaits further investigation.

ERAS AND PERIODS LONGER THAN A YEAR

Of periods longer than a year the primitive mind had but the vaguest conceptions. Indeed primitive men may entirely lack the conception of even a year. In the Philippines the Bontoc Igorots have no notion of a year. It is of course possible to count a series of years without any notion of the year itself. The Bataks of Sumatra use smallpox epidemics as marking off periods, usually nine to twelve years in length, and a native will say that his house is "two smallpox epidemics old." The Hottentots keep records of the ages of their livestock by the number of calvings or lambings. But among people of lower intelligence there is no conception of a long period of time. A Dahomey Negro rarely knows how old he is, and we are all familiar with the old darky who has no idea of his age.

With the advance of civilization man's increasing knowledge has had a profound influence upon his conceptions of time, and especially his discernment of ever lengthening periods of time. The astonishingly long reigns claimed for their early rulers by the scribes of Egypt and Babylonia must have been compiled in a primitive age of naïve and childish fancies, whose fantastically impossible periods could not have grown out of any just impressions of time as measured by human history. The flow of time was not at first revealed to him by the processes of nature. The erosion of a river valley and its changing contours would not be discernible, because the early observer had no knowledge of how those contours looked one thousand years earlier. But when he saw a huge pyramid with gaping holes gnawed into its flanks by the biting sandblast which the powerful Egyptian north wind drove against it, he knew just how that pyramid slope had looked when it left the hands of the architect a thousand years earlier. Thus the slow decay of the works of man taught him what the processes of nature could not at first have revealed. Such unwritten human records in Babylonia and Egypt began to reveal to men after 3000 B.C. the slow march of time, which became more and more evident as those records gradually took written form. The earliest known annals of a nation compiled in the twenty-eighth century B.C. covered some fifteen hundred years of human history, that is, they extended from the forty-third to the twenty-eighth century B.C. The men of the Pharaoh's court, therefore, in the twenty-eighth century B.C., that is, some four thousand seven hundred years ago, could look back upon a lapse of time a little longer than that which we survey as we contemplate the period that lies between us and the so-called fall of Rome in A.D. 476. For

[91]

those men time had long since ceased to be a discontinuous duration. The earliest mention of an era appears on a monument of Ramses II in the thirteenth century B.C., a monument which is dated in the year 400 of an era which had begun about 1720 B.C.

In Babylonia the cycle of nineteen years for the intercalation of the lunar months evidently discloses a conception of time as a continuous flow of duration. It was introduced in 528 B.C.

SCIENCE AND THE CONTINUOUS FLOW OF TIME

It is evident that historical impressions of the long and continuous flow of time, especially for some centuries before the beginning of the Christian Era, had led the men of the Hellenistic Age and the early Roman Empire to their dreams of a thousand years, which have left us the rather misleading significance of the word "millennium" as a "golden age."

It is rather natural science than human history which has so enormously expanded our modern conception of the flow of time. About 400 B.C. the Chaldean astronomer Kidinnu, whom the Greeks called Kidenas, discovered the procession of the equinoxes, involving a cycle of twenty-six thousand years. That was the longest period revealed by the vast celestial clock for many centuries, indeed, perhaps even into modern times. It was followed by the geologists' estimates of the length of the periods required for the formation of the earth. Much more precise are their computations of the length of the much later process which has produced the present surface of the globe. In our prehistoric survey of Northeastern Africa, it has been possible to date the desiccation of North Africa in the middle of the Old Stone Age, and to show that the sand dunes of Nubia as they marched southward left the North African coast of the Mediterranean about thirty-five thousand years ago. The computations of De Geers have shown that it is about nine thousand years since the retreating ice of the Glacial Age reached its present latitude, while the investigations of the American geologists would indicate that the Ice Age began probably a million years ago. Such researches, especially the field investigations of our own prehistoric survey in Northeastern Africa, have revealed to us this imposing panorama of terrestrial processes as the vast stage where we discern earliest man emerging as the only implement-making creature, whose prehistoric life is thus disclosed interlocking with the processes of nature, which formed our globe. It is a tremendous spectacle: the geological process marching hand in hand with the cultural advance of man.

Such disclosures of the position of man in the universe form for us the culmination of man's sense of time as a historical process no longer discontinuous. We begin to feel a range of time measured by the emergence of the life of man in the universe, until we are aware that there is no time apart from man. Those celestial processes with which our knowledge of duration now begins, as they are disclosed to us in incomprehensible gulfs of millions of light years, are for us essentially timeless. We now recognize that modern investigation of early man has revealed him to us filling the gap between the incalculable duration of the celestial processes on the one hand and on the other the more comprehensible periods of the terrestrial processes that formed our globe as the home of man and led over to the historic age. Thus in vastly remote prehistoric ages, when the present surface of our globe was being fashioned by geological forces, we begin to see man, all unconscious of those forces about him, but suddenly revealed to us rising out of them and entering a realm of time, because he was, and still is, the first and only creature to be aware of time. He was its creator, the first being possessed of the ability to look back along his own trail and to recognize the point in the timeless process of the universe where the creature man entered a new and mysterious realm, which by that very fact made him the creator of a domain of time.

INDEX

INDEX

Africa, prehistoric survey of North-eastern, 92-93

Age, of the universe, 39-40; of the sun and stars, 26, 27, 51

Alexander the Great, 85, 87

Alice in Wonderland, 3-4, 11, 12, 16, 19

Amenemhet, first clockmaker, 84-87

Amenhotep III, 84

Andromeda Nebula, 48, 49, 54

Angle-measurement system, 7

Arabs, natural phenomena determined year for, 65; their astronomers may have divided the hour, 89

Aristotle, 88

Arthur, James, lectures, 23, 40, 43

Astronomers, calculations by, for age of sun and stars, 26, 27, 51; aspects of time of interest to, 39-40; Chaldean, 74, 90, 92; possible division of hour by Arabian, 89

Astronomical instrument, oldest, 82

Astronomy, importance of the number 360 in, 69-70

Astrophysical time scale, 50-51

Babylonians, originators of lunar month, 63; calendar of, 63-64, 73; 360-day year, 69-70; calculated the solar year, 74; division of day, 77, 88; no timepieces have survived, 90; record of time, 91, 92

Biological evidences of the age of the earth, 31-32

Bok, Dr., 50

Borchardt, 70, 71, 82

Breasted, James H., first reliable date in history computed by, 5, 70-72

Caesar, Julius, introduced the Egyptian calendar in the Roman Empire, 73, 74-75

Calculus invented by Leibnitz and Newton, 12

Calendar, Greek, 62-63, 67, 68; Egyptian, 63, 64, 69-70, 73, 74-75; Babylonian, 63-64, 69-70, 73; Darius introduced the Egyptian, in the Persian Empire, 64; Mohammed adopted the lunar, 64, 66; Jewish church, 64-65, Gregorian, 64; source of European, 73-75

Censorinus, 71

Chaldean astronomers, 74, 90, 92

Charlemagne, 86

Charles V, of France, clock made for, 10

Civilizations, accomplishments of ancient, 32-33

Clepsydra, description of, 7-8, 83-86

Clocks, history of mechanical, 9-10; more accurate timekeepers than rotation of earth, 42-43; astronomical, 43-44; striking clock shifted beginning of day from dawn to midnight, 77; earliest, 78-86; stellar, 80-83; Amenemhet's clock, 84-86; mechanical clocks introduced during Hellenistic Age, 85; striking clock helped to fix uniform hour length, 88. See also Clepsydra

[97]

Index

Compton effects, discovery of, 17

Continuity of nature, concept of, 10, 11-12

Copernican thesis, 4; attitude of sixteenth-century writers toward, 4-5

Cosmic perspective, 45-47

Cosmic-ray effects, discovery of, 17

Darius the Great, 73; introduced the Egyptian calendar in the Persian Empire, 64

Darwin, continuity of evolution, 31-32; *Voyage of the Beagle*, 31; *Origin of Species*, 32-33

Day, 76-77; most fundamental measure of time, 6; division of, into hours, 7, 87-88

De Geers, 93

de Sitter, 51

Diogenes, 87

Earth, 3, 40, 41; age of the, 26-32, 51, 52, 53, 92-93; effect on rotation of structure and planets, 43; Egyptians unaware of motions of, 79

East Indians, natural phenomena determined year for, 65-66

Eddington, 51, 53

Egypt, time-measurement in, 5-7, 77-87, 91-92; division of day in, 77

Egyptian calendar, 63, 64; stellar year, 65; stellar observations basis of, 65, 68; seasons of year in, 67; early observation of heavens in, 68; 360-day year, 69-70; 365-day year, 70-71; importance of, 72-73; social requirements influenced, 72-73; source of European calendar, 73-75

Einstein and theory of relativity, 15-16

Electrons, 17, 18-19

Energy and time, 18, 23-24

Equinoxes, Egyptian sun clock fitted to length of day at, 79; discovery of procession of, 92

Eras and periods longer than a year, 90-92

Eudoxus, 74

European calendar, Egyptian source of, 73-75

Evolution, 51; continuity of, 31-32

Fitzgerald and Lorentz, shortening of the measuring rod, 15, 16

Fluxions, 12

Galaxy, lifetime of a, 39-40; Milky Way, 44-45; description of, 47; age of our own, 52, 53; recession of, 52-53; nature of our own supergalaxy, 53-54

Galileo, 11, 12, 13, 17; inventor of pendulum clock, 9, 10; inventor of thermometer, 9

Geography, importance of the number 360 in, 69-70

Geological estimate of the age of the earth, 26-31, 92-93

Glacial Age, 93

Grand Canyon, a record of time, 28-31

Greece, time-measurement in, 8; calendar based on moon, 62-63, 64, 73; division of day in, 77, 87-88

Gregorian calendar, 64, 74-75

Hammurabi, 63

Harun al-Raschid, 86

Harvard Observatory, 46, 49, 55

Hebrews. See Jews

Index

Hegira, the year of the, 64
Heisenberg principle of uncertainty, 18
Heliopolis, 70
Herodotus, 73, 88
Hesiod observed stellar movements in his calendar, 67, 68
Hipparchus, 74
Hippocrates, 90
History, value of, 34; earliest fixed date in, 5, 70-72
Homer, 88
Hour, division of, into minutes and seconds, 7, 88-90; division of day into, 77, 88-89; hour scale imperfect on Egyptian sun clock, 79; determination of, 80; not of uniform length, 86-87, 88; twenty-four-hour day, 87-88
Hubble, 53
Hyades, 49, 50

Intercalation, 63, 64-65
Interferometers, Michelson's, 13
Intergalactic spaces, 45
Italy, first sun clock in, 87-88

Jews, intercalation and solar year, 64-65; natural phenomena determined year, 65; religious significance of rest day, 75-76
Jupiter, time on, 42

Kennedy, Dr. Roy S., 16
Kidinnu discovered procession of equinoxes, 92
Koran, 64

Laplace, 19
Leibnitz and Newton invented calculus, 12
Life, effect of views regarding time on, 35-36

Light, wave length of, as timekeeper, 43
Light year, 47, 48, 55
Lindemann, F. A., 19
Lorentz. See Fitzgerald
Luni-solar year, 61-65
Luxor, 83, 84

Macroscopic phenomena, 17
Magellanic Clouds, 48-50, 51, 52, 54
Man, historical record of, 25-26, 32-33; cultures of, 32-33; influence of Egyptian calendar on, 75-76
Master-and-slave clocks of the Shortt design, 43
Measurement of time, 5-18, 25-26, 40, 41, 52, 55, 59-94
Mechanics, basis of, 9, 16; influence of theory of relativity on, 15
Megaparsec, 47
Mercury, time-measurement on, 40, 41
Meridian, circle used to measure rotation and time, 42; observations of, earliest time measurer, 82
Merkhet, description of, 80-82, 82n
Merneptah, sundial of, 80
Messier 33. See Andromeda Nebula
Metagalaxy, 47, 54, 55
Meton, 63
Michelson-Morley experiment, 12, 14, 15, 16
Microscopic phenomena, studies of, 17-18
Middle Ages, Egyptian hour of varying length used until end of, 88; subdivision of hour not known until end of, 89

Index

Milky Way, 44-45
Millikan, Dr. R. A., 23
Minutes, 7, 88-90
Mohammed adopted lunar calendar, 64, 66
Moon, first measure of continuous time, 61-65, 73; twelve in year, 62
Moon-month, incommensurable with year, 62-64, 66, 73
Month, divorced from moon in Egyptian calendar, 70; origin of, 75; inconsistency in names of, 75; Amenemhet's observations on length of nights, 84. See also Moon-month
Morley. See Michelson
Motion, measurement of, 23

Nabu-rimannu computed solar year, 74
Natural law, concept of, 10-11
Natural science expands present conception of time, 92-94
Nature's phases caused early observance of year, 61-62, 65, 67, 90-91, 92
Near East originator of division of day into hours, 77
Newton, 11, 12, 13, 17
Night, 7-8, 68, 76-77, 84, 86-87, 88
Nile, inundations of, and rising of Sirius, 6, 67; early observation of heavens on banks of, 68
Norman Bridge Laboratory, experiments at, 16

Oriental Institute, The, 82n
Oscillating crystals, 43

Pendulum clock invented by Galileo, 9, 10
Persia, lunar year adopted by, 63-
64; Egyptian calendar introduced into, 64; Babylonian astronomers and, 73
Photoelectric effects, discovery of, 17
Photons, 17
Physical world, description of, in terms of new discoveries, 17
Physicist, calculations by, for age of sun and stars, 26, 27
Planck's h units, 17, 18
Planet Number 3. See Earth
Planets, time reckoning on other, 41-42
Pleiades, 49, 50, 67
Plummet a part of Egyptian sun clock, 79, 81
Primitive ways of measuring time, 60-61, 65-66, 90
Protons, 17
Ptolemy, 89
Ptolemy Euergetes I, 74
Pulse, clepsydra used to count, 8n; pendulum clock used to count, 9; may have been counted by Egyptian surgeons, 89-90
Pyramids, and temples, used as time-measuring instruments, 6-7; Texts mention hour division of day, 77; helped Egyptians realize flow of time, 91-92

Quanta, development of facts and theory of, 17-19; conclusions drawn from, 18-19

Radioactivity, process of, used to measure age of earth, 52
Ramadhân, observance of, 64
Ramses II, 92
Ramses VI, 83
Ramses IX, 83
Recorde, Robert, 4-5
Relativity, 13, 15; special theory

Index

of, 15-16; conclusions drawn from; 18-19; explanation of expansion of universe through theory of, 52-53

Rest day, universal connection between religion and, 75-76

Roman Empire, time-measurement in, 7-8, 87-88; Egyptian calendar introduced in, by Julius Caesar, 73, 74-75

Rotation of earth dominates our time concept, 41, 42, 43; effect of structure of earth on, 43

Saturn, measurement of rotation period of, 14; time on, 42

Science, beginnings of, 6; and the continuous flow of time, 92-94

Seasons, in prehistoric Egypt, 67; in 365-day calendar, 70; Egyptian sun clock did not provide for changing, 79

Seconds, 7, 88-90

Sexagesimal system, 7, 69, 89

Shortt design, master-and-slave clocks of the, 43

Sirius, used as computer of time, 5, 6, 67, 68-69, 70, 71, 73-74, 83; age of, compared with the Sun, 51

Snefru, King, 81

Social requirements influenced Egyptian calendar, 72-73

Space, time independent of, up to twentieth century, 12; relativity of, 15-16; space-time concept, 23-24, 39

Spectroscopic effects, discovery of, 17

Stars, time-measurement by, 5, 7, 43-44, 78; age of, 26, 27, 51

Star-table, 82-83

Sumerian. See Sexagesimal system

Sun, estimates of age of, 26, 27, 51; did not furnish early man with length of year, 65, 66, 68; movements of, used in time-measurement, 78-79; Egyptians unaware of motions of, 79

Sun clocks, 7, 78-80, 87-88. See also Sundials

Sundials, 7, 80

Supergalaxy, nature of our own, 53-54

Temperature, measurement of individual, 9

Thales, 73

Thebes, 84

Thermometer invented by Galileo, 9

Thorndyke, Dr. Edward L., 16

Thutmose III, 79-80

Thutmose IV, 82n

Tidal interaction between earth, sun, and moon causes irregularities in rotation, 42-43

Time, modern conception of, 3, 24, 92-93; ancient conception of, 5-9, 60-61, 65-66, 90; measurement of, 5-18, 25-26, 40, 41, 52, 55, 59-94; new conception of, in sixteenth and seventeenth centuries, 9, 11; independent of space up to twentieth century, 12; relativity of, 16, 39; energy and, 18, 23-24; interpretation of, 23; historical, 24-27, 59-94; value to life, 35-36; and the astronomer, 39-40, 42; rotation of the earth and, 41; terms used to indicate, 50, 51-52; continual flow of, 60, 91, 92-94; measuring devices, 77-86; timetables, 82-83; record of, in Egypt, 91

Timepieces. See Clocks

Time-rate-of-change, 9, 10, 23

Index

Time scale, long, 50-51; short, 51

Truth, impermanence of all but, 33-34

Tutenkhamon, 82n

Universe, age of the, 39-40; expansion of the, 52-53

Velocity, 9, 10, 18, 23

Venus, time on, 41-42

Water clocks, 83-86; used by Egyptians, Greeks, and Romans, 7-8; introduced into Rome, 88

Wave-theory of light, 13-15

Week, 75-76

Westminster clock, 9-10

X-ray effects, discovery of, 17

Year, one of the earliest measures of time, 6, 92; luni-solar, 61-65; nature's phases caused early observance of, 61-62; determination of length of, 65; stellar, 65-68; rise of Nile beginning of Egyptian, 67; 360-day, 69-70; 365-day, 70-71; earliest computation of solar, 73-74; eras and periods longer than a, 90-92. See also Light year

Zimmern, 69